CONTENTS

PRANK SQUAD

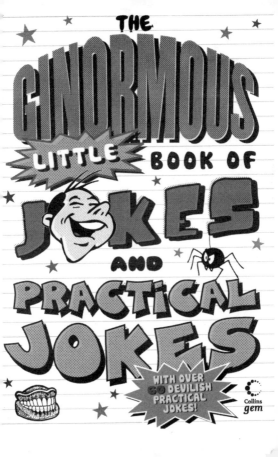

The Ginormous Little Book of Jokes and Practical Jokes
Copyright © 2009. All rights reserved.
Published by Collins, an imprint of HarperCollins Publishers Ltd.
First Canadian edition

HarperCollins books may be purchased for educational, business,
or sales promotional use through our Special Markets Department.

HarperCollins Publishers Ltd
2 Bloor Street East, 20th Floor
Toronto, Ontario, Canada
M4W IA8

www.harpercollins.ca

Library and Archives Canada Cataloguing in Publication
The ginormous little book of jokes and practical jokes.
ISBN 978-1-55468-507-3
I. Canadian wit and humor. 2. Practical jokes.
PN6178.C3G56 2009 C818'.602 C2009-903162-0

Printed and bound in Canada
9 8 7 6 5 4 3 2 I

THE MAKING
OF A
COMEDIAN

Step 1: What Is a Joke Made Of?

What makes a joke a joke?

First is the *set-up*. Launch right into the joke. Make sure you know the whole thing—there's nothing quite as embarrassing as realizing you forgot the funny part.

Next is *timing*. Comedic timing is a skill that takes lots and lots of practice to perfect. Don't rush through your joke. But don't wait too long or your audience will lose interest.

Finally: the *punchline*. This is the last part of a joke—the part you've been building up to. It's the funny part. Tell it loudly and firmly. Don't laugh in the middle of it. The punchline should have an effect like its name—a punch of silliness, right to the funny bone.

Step 2: Rehearsing

Although many comedy routines sound as though they were made up on the spur of the moment, every good comedian spends a great deal of time rehearsing. Even improv comedians have to practise! Rehearsal helps you make your routine smooth. You need to practise your pacing: when to pause, what to emphasize. You need to set the right tone: cheerful, sombre, sarcastic.

Every professional comedian has spent time practising the art of joke telling and has studied his or her punchlines really well. Just remember, if an audience thinks that you don't know what you're doing, they'll be too uncomfortable to laugh even if you've said something hilarious.

Step 3: Plotting Your Strategy

If you were able to convince someone to buy you this book, you've mastered the first principle of joke telling: strategy. Strategy is one of the most important tools in the comedian's box of tricks. It's how you plan your act to make people laugh when you want them to laugh. The secret to influencing others is to have confidence in yourself. You are the one onstage, under the spotlight—you have the power. So don't apologize before you tell a joke—especially one that comes from this book.

Step 4: Sequencing

Telling a joke can produce a chuckle, but telling two or three jokes in the proper sequence can have your audience rolling on the floor. The classic joke sequence is the "Why did the chicken cross the road?" series, where the punchline or question varies slightly with each telling. This method works really well for two reasons: first, your listener is already warmed up and wants to keep laughing; second, you're playing off an expectation. The audience expects to hear the classic joke but instead gets a new, alternate joke. This makes the joke twice as funny. It's like a clown hitting someone in the face with a pie and his victim then asking for ice cream on the side.

Step 5: Embellishing

Many of you have probably already mastered this one. Joke telling is just about the only time when lying is a good thing. Lying is allowed, and even necessary, in comedy, because jokes are usually made up anyway.

We all know that animals don't really talk or drive cars in real life, but they definitely do in the world of comedy.

When you get really good at telling the jokes in this book, try adding stuff on to them. This is called *embellishing*. In the world of comedy, good joke tellers embellish to make their jokes sillier, dumber or funnier. Just remember: the more absurd the lies you tell, the funnier your jokes will be.

Step 6: Don't Give It All Away!

We didn't just give these jokes away, did we? Well, neither should you. Never, ever blurt out a punchline before its time. You shouldn't ask people if they've heard the joke before, because you might give yourself away in the process. A funny joke is like a well-planned surprise party—the bigger the surprise, the happier the party.

And Finally, a Special Note about Practical Jokes!

Before you try a practical joke, you have to remember some important things:

Practical jokes must always be harmless. Be extra cautious about food allergies.

Never do anything illegal or anything that might be dangerous.

Never do anything that might hurt someone.

Know your customers—the victim should be someone who can take it.

And never forget, the element of surprise is always important.

FUNNY
QUESTIONS,
FUNNIER
ANSWERS

If a seagull flies over the sea, what flies over the bay?
A ba-gel.

If a nut on a wall is a walnut, what is a nut in the washroom?
A pee-can.

What boats talk?
Kay-yaks.

What did Mickey Mouse say when Minnie asked if he was listening?
I'm all ears.

What did the baker think of the joke?
He got a rise out of it.

What did the judge say when the skunk came in to testify?
Odour in the court!

What did the spider bride wear when she got married?
A webbing dress.

What do caribou have that no other animal has?
Baby caribou.

What goes best with toast when you're in a car?
Traffic jam.

What goes bonk, bonk, bonk, bonk, bonk?
A rubber-nosed clown falling down a flight of stairs.

What goes bonk, bonk, bonk, bonk, croak?
A rubber-nosed clown who's just been changed into a frog by an evil witch.

What goes bonk, bonk, bonk, bonk, dunk?
A rubber-nosed clown being dribbled by a professional basketball player.

What goes tick, tick, woof, woof?
A watch dog.

What happened to the woman whom the magician sawed in half?
She's living in Calgary and Montreal.

What happens to spoons that work too much?
They go stir-crazy.

What happens when you annoy a clock?
It gets ticked off.

What happens when you throw a clock in the air?
Time's up.

What is a musician's favourite cereal?
Flute Loops.

What kind of bee is the smartest?
A spelling bee.

What kind of books do skunks read?
Best-smellers.

What sporting event do people from Venus, Mars, Saturn and Mercury watch on TV every October?
The Out-of-This-World Series.

What's a dinosaur's favourite province?
B.C.

What's a werewolf's favourite day of the week?
Moonday.

What's the opposite of a hotdog?
A chili dog.

When does it rain in the circus?
When the man on the flying tra-pees.

Where were you born?
Ontario.
What part?
All of me.

**Who lives in Prince
Edward Island and bakes
funny-coloured bread and
rolls?**
Anne of Green Bagels.

**Why are leopards no good
at hide-and-seek?**
*Because they're always
spotted.*

**Why couldn't anyone find
the deck of cards?**
It got lost in the shuffle.

Why couldn't the concertgoer get her money back when the singer was off-key?
Because she paid the flat rate.

Why do parents carry their babies?
Because babies aren't big enough to carry their parents.

Why shouldn't you short-change a skunk?
It's bound to make a stink.

Can you can a piano?
No, but you can tun-a fish.

How can you tell the difference between a judge and a skating rink?
One brings people to justice; the other brings people to just ice.

How did Minnie Mouse save
Mickey from drowning?
*She gave him mouse-to-mouse
resuscitation.*

Why was the teacher
cross-eyed?
*Because he couldn't control
his pupils.*

Why was the water fountain
taken to court?
For being drunk in a public place.

PRANK SQUAD

RIPPED PANTS: Make someone think they ripped their pants. Place an object on the floor (a coin or book works well). Stand nearby, holding a scrap of cloth that is easy to rip. (Test it first, to make sure it has a good ripping sound. You can also use a piece of Velcro.) Then, when the person bends down, r-i-p the cloth. The victim is sure to think he's ripped his pants and will start checking (probably around his backside) for the damage.

NON-CLEANING SOAP: Use clear nail polish to coat a bar of soap, and let it dry. The victim won't be able to figure out why it's impossible to get a lather going.

DAFFY
DEFINITIONS

What do you call a boy who's been mauled by a bull?
Gord.

What do you call a camel without a hump?
Humphrey.

What do you call a boy hanging on the wall?
Art.

What do you call a boy onstage?
Mike.

What do you call a man who has been buried for 100 years?
Pete.

What do you call a man who owes money?
Bill.

What do you call a man with a shovel stuck in his head?
Doug.

What do you call a man without a shovel stuck in his head?
Douglas.

What do you call a dog with no legs?
Matt.

What do you call a baby bird that takes after its father?
A chirp off the old beak.

What do you call a bird that's been eaten by a cat?
A swallow.

What do you call a couple of surgeons?
A paradox.

What do you call a dinosaur that's always on time?
A prontosaurus.

What do you call a dog that helps you carry hot things?
An oven mutt.

**What do you call a
pirate who always
skips school?**
Captain Hooky.

**What do you call a fish
with no eyes?**
A fsh.

What do you call
a fish's date?
His gill-friend.

**What do you call a gorilla with a
green thumb?**
Hairy Potter.

What do you call a grizzly bear with no teeth?
A gummy bear.

What do you call a group of mice in costume?
A mousequerade party.

What do you call a keyboard with good morals?
An upright piano.

What do you call a king's sore throat?
A royal pain in the neck.

What do you call a large gorilla who likes to dance?
King Conga.

What do you call a mouse that hangs out with a bunch of pythons?
Lunch.

What do you call a person who puts poison in someone's cornflakes?
A cereal killer.

What do you call a pooch who wakes up too early in the morning?
A groggy doggie.

What do you call a really good camel joke?
A hump-dinger.

What do you call a reptile who hangs out in bars?
A lounge lizard.

What do you call a robot that always takes the longest route?
R2 Detour.

What do you call a Roman emperor when he catches a cold?
Julius Sneezer.

What do you call a shabby teddy?
Thread-bear.

What do you call a shark fin floating in your soup?
A dorsal morsel.

What do you call a sheep farm with only rams?
Ewes-less.

What do you call a student who can subtract, multiply and divide, but can't add?
A total failure.

What do you call a super-pig who can climb up the side of buildings?
Spiderham.

What do you call a woman who no longer owes any money?
Bernadette.

What do you call a woman with a sheep on her head?
Baa-baa-rah.

What do you call a moustached woman who visits you in the night and grants you three wishes?
Your hairy godmother.

What do you call an angle that's gotten into a car crash?
A rectangle.

What do you call an insect that goes "Buzz-mzz-ummz-mzz"?
A mumble bee.

What do you call Roller-bladers who chat on the computer?
Online skaters.

What do you call the second bird that's been eaten by the same cat?
An after-dinner tweet.

What do you call two banana peels?
A pair of slippers.

PRANK SQUAD

CD CHAOS: Mix up your friend's CDs. If they're stacked, open the top CD case and remove the CD. Place it in the second case from the top. Place the second CD in the third case from the top. Repeat the process right down to the bottom CD, which will now go inside the top CD case.

SILLY SHOPPING: Ask your brother or sister to run an errand for you—say you need something for a school project. The item you need may sound real but doesn't exist: a can of striped paint, smooth sandpaper, a left-handed monkey wrench or a dozen buttonholes. You can also ask for a "long weight." If the store owner has a sense of humour, the wait may be a really long one.

JOKE-A-RAMA

"Are caterpillars good to eat?" asked a little boy at the dinner table.

"No," said his father. "What makes you ask a question like that?"

"You had one on your salad, but it's gone now."

"I'm going to be a famous magician," said Justin to his father, "because I can make a golf ball float."

Justin's father was very curious. "And how do you do that?" he asked.

"Well, it's very scientific. It requires some magic ingredients," said Justin.

Justin's father leaned forward in his chair. "Oh, really," he said. "And what are they?"

"Well, the golf ball, of course. And then two scoops of ice cream and some root beer."

A boastful Texan was sightseeing in Toronto. "What's that building over there?" he asked his cab driver.

"That's the Royal Ontario Museum."

"Oh," bragged the Texan. "We could build that in two weeks."

Next he asked, "What's that building?"

"Well," said the cabbie, "that's the Eaton Centre."

"Hmm," said the Texan. "Back home we can build a place like that in a week."

A few minutes later they passed the CN Tower. "Hey," the tourist asked, "what's that?"

"Don't know," replied the cab driver. "It wasn't there this morning."

A broccoli, a tomato and a yam competed in a race. The broccoli got off to a great start but, being a green runner, didn't have the strength to finish. The yam and the tomato were neck and neck for the first stretch, but then the tomato fell far behind. The yam almost won, but collapsed in exhaustion right before the finish line. Over the following hour, the tomato managed to run the entire distance, and won the race.

Why was it so successful?

The tomato paste itself.

A computer rolled into a bakery and went up to the counter. There were doughnuts and muffins and pastries, but the computer pointed at a plate of cookies. "Hello," it said in its electronic voice.

Astonished, the person behind the counter replied, "Wow, we don't get too many computers in this store. Do you want some of these cookies?"

"Well," said the computer, "I might. Could you tell me how many bites are in each one?"

"I'm sorry," said the server. "There aren't any bytes in these cookies, just chips."

A duck walked into a restaurant and asked the waiter, "Do you have any olives?"

The waiter said, "We don't serve ducks in our restaurant. You'll have to leave."

So the duck went away and came back five minutes later. Again he asked the waiter, "Do you have any olives?"

Again the waiter replied, "We don't allow ducks, and you'll have to leave. If you come here again, I will staple your feet to the floor."

An hour later the duck showed up again and asked, "Do you have any staples?"

The waiter replied, "NO!"

"Good," the duck said. "Then do you have any olives?"

A fire started near a farm. The fire department was called in, but the fire was more than they could handle. Someone suggested calling the volunteer firefighers. They arrived in a beat-up truck, rumbled toward the fire, drove into the middle of the flames and stopped. Then they jumped off the truck and sprayed water in all directions. Soon they had broken the blaze into two smaller parts that they easily put out.

The farmer was so grateful that he presented the volunteers with a cheque for $1,000. A reporter asked the volunteer fire captain what the department planned to do with the funds. "That should be obvious," he replied. "The first thing we're going to do is get the brakes fixed on our fire truck!"

It was lunchtime at the factory, and Sam opened his brown bag and took out his sandwich. As he unwrapped it, he grumbled, "Peanut butter and jam, peanut butter and jam. Every day it's peanut butter and jam. I am sick of peanut butter and jam."

"So," asked Craig, "why don't you ask for something different for a change?"

"I can't," Sam told him. "I make my own lunch."

A frog expert from the aquarium gave a talk to a grade three class. "It's easy to tell the male frogs from the female frogs," she said. "When you feed them, the male frogs will eat only female flies, and the female frogs will eat only male flies."

"But how do you know which flies are male and which are female?" asked a boy sitting at the back of the class.

"How am I supposed to know?" replied the woman. "I'm a frog expert."

A little boy returned from the grocery store with his dad. While his dad put away the groceries, the little boy opened his box of animal crackers and spread them all over the kitchen table.

"What are you doing?" asked his dad.

"The box says you shouldn't eat them if the seal is broken," said the little boy. "I'm looking for the seal."

A little boy was practising the violin in the living room while his mother was trying to read in the den. The family dog was lying in the den, and as the screeching sounds of the violin reached the dog's ears, he began to howl loudly. The mother listened to the dog and the violin for as long as she could. Then she jumped up, dropped her paper to the floor, and shouted above the noise, "For goodness' sake, can't you play something the dog doesn't know?"

A dog with a bandaged foot limped into town one day.

The sheriff approached the stranger and said, "What brings you to Dawson City?"

The dog replied, "I'm looking for the man who shot my paw."

One day, a flying saucer lands in Ottawa and tries to park in the middle of the sidewalk. Immediately a traffic cop rushes over and says to the Martian, "You can't park that thing here. Go find a legal spot."

The Martian looks up at the cop and says, "Take me to your meter."

The Fathers of Confederation couldn't come up with a name for their new country, so they decided to place all the letters of the alphabet into a drawer and work with the first three they picked. When John A. Macdonald pulled out the first letter, he said, "C, eh?" After picking the second letter, he said, "N, eh?" And after the last letter he declared, "D, eh?" And that's how Canada got its name.

A fish needed surgery but didn't know if she'd be able to pay for it. She met with the doctor to talk about how much it would cost. "Don't worry at all," said the doctor. "I'll give you a discount on the price. I admire and respect your cousin, so I am honoured to be taking care of his family. He is, beyond any doubt, an excellent sturgeon."

A little girl became ill and was taken to the hospital. It was her first time away from home and she began to cry. The nurse was concerned and asked the little girl if she was homesick.

"No," said the girl. "I'm here sick!"

A millipede ran into a centipede on the street. The millipede said in surprise, "Wow, what are the odds of this?!"

"Oh," answered the centipede, "about 10 to 1."

A sparkplug drives up to a Tim Hortons and orders a coffee. "Okay," says the cashier. "Just don't start anything."

A mom walks into a store and asks if she could have a toy tractor for her daughter. The store clerk replies, "I'm sorry, ma'am, but we don't do exchanges."

Joe was late meeting Sarah at the corner, and his shorts and T-shirt were all wet. He said he had been playing in the sprinkler but couldn't dry his clothes.

"Why not?" asked Sarah.

"Because I couldn't fit in the dryer."

Kim: "I had a nightmare last night."

Tim: "What did you dream about?"

Kim: "I dreamed I was eating Shreddies."

Tim: "What's so bad about that?"

Kim: "When I woke up, half the pillow was gone."

A private eye had just moved into her new office when there was a knock at the door. She wanted to make a good impression, so she yelled, "Come in!" and picked up the phone, pretending to be talking to someone important. The visitor waited patiently, and after a minute the detective hung up the phone and said, "As you can see, I'm very busy. What can I do for you?"

"Not much," replied the visitor. "I'm here to hook up your phone."

A snail is mugged by three turtles. When the police ask the snail to give a description of what happened, all he can say is, "I don't know, officer. It all happened so fast!"

Want to hear a joke about bowling?
Spare me.

Did you ever wonder . . . what was the best thing *before* sliced bread?

Jack couldn't mow the lawn because he sprained his ankle. What do you think his dad said to that?
That's a lame excuse.

A tourist was fishing off the coast of Florida when his boat tipped over. He could swim, but he was afraid of alligators, so he hung on to the side of the overturned boat. Spotting an old beachcomber standing on the shore, the tourist shouted out, "Are there any 'gators around here?"

"Naw," the man hollered back. "They haven't been around here for years!"

Feeling safe, the tourist started swimming calmly toward the shore. About halfway there, he shouted again, "How'd you get rid of the 'gators?"

"We didn't do anything," said the beachcomber. "The sharks got 'em."

A woman walks into a bar with a giraffe. The woman goes over to the bar to order a drink while the giraffe lies down. The bartender says to the woman, "Hey, you can't leave that lyin' on the floor!"

The woman answers, "It's not a lion."

An old man was lying in bed, preparing to die, surrounded by his loved ones. Suddenly, he smelled a wonderful aroma of cookies baking. He turned to his wife and said weakly, "Ahh, all I want before I leave this Earth is one of your delicious cookies."

"No way," she told him. "I'm saving them for the funeral."

Announcement at railway station: "Will passengers taking the 5:35 train from Montreal to Halifax kindly put it back."

Every time I get on the ferry to Victoria, it makes me cross.

Jackie: "Mom, where were you born?"
Mom: "Vancouver."
Jackie: "Where was Dad born?"
Mom: "Winnipeg."
Jackie: "And where was I born?"
Mom: "Toronto."
Jackie: "Cool—isn't it great that we
all got together?"

**Last night my school orchestra
played Beethoven.**
Beethoven lost.

Jordan was playing in the schoolyard when he fell down and broke his right arm. Kate came running up to him with a big smile on her face. "Wow, Jordan, you're so lucky. Now you don't have to take any exams."

"Actually, I'm really unlucky," replied Jordan.

"What makes you say that?" she asked.

"I'm left-handed," Jordan moaned. "I meant to fall on my other arm."

Justin: "What did you get that little
 medal for?"
Amanda: "For singing."
Justin: "And what did you get that big
 medal for?"
Amanda: "For stopping."

Emily went to visit the new baby at
the Johnsons' house. Mrs. Johnson
answered the door and Emily said,
"Hi, Mrs. Johnson, is baby Ben
there? Could I talk to him?"

Mrs. Johnson smiled and said,
"I'm sorry, but Ben is only a little
baby. He can't talk yet."

Emily said, "That's okay, I'll
wait."

Little Paige always looked forward to her lunch, and today Paige's dad was excited about the new treat he had planned for her. Paige's dad laid a carefully arranged plate on the table and then went to the kitchen to get some lemonade. He was completely confused when he came back to see Paige crying at the table.

"What's wrong, Paige? Don't you like the animal crackers I bought for you?" asked her dad.

Paige just cried harder and wailed, "But, Daddy, we're vegetarians!"

Mother: "Eat your broccoli. It's good
for growing children."
Kid: "Who wants to grow children?"

One day a little girl put her shoes
on by herself for the first time. Her
mother noticed that her left shoe was
on her right foot.

"Honey," said the mom, "I think
your shoes are on the wrong feet."

The little girl looked up and said,
"No, Mom, I *know* these are my feet."

Noah: "Did you like the book about the
porcupine?"
Julie: "Up to a point."

Some Boy Scouts from the city were on a camping trip. The mosquitoes were so fierce that the boys had to hide under their blankets to avoid being bitten. Then one of them saw some lightning bugs and said to his friend, "We might as well give up. They're coming after us with flashlights."

They say that Isaac Newton discovered the law of gravity when an apple fell on his head. *Was it a laptop or a desktop model?*

Two boys were camping in the back-yard. Late at night they started wondering what time it was. "Start singing really loudly," the one boy suggested.

"How will that help?" asked the other boy.

"Just do it," insisted the first. They both started singing as loudly as they could. Moments later, a neighbour threw open her window and shouted, "Keep it down! Don't you know it's three o'clock in the morning?"

Two goldfish are in a tank. One says to the other, "Do you know how to drive this thing?"

PRANK SQUAD

CONFETTI SHOWER: Here's a trick for a rainy day (or evening). If friends (or friends of your parents) are visiting and they bring umbrellas, wait until nobody's looking. Open each umbrella partway, pour confetti inside, close it, and then return it to where it was. When the friends leave and open their umbrellas, they'll get an unexpected shower of confetti snow.

CHALK BOTTOM: Place a piece of chalk between two sheets of paper, and pound it into a powder. Then sprinkle a little of the chalk powder on a chair before someone special sits down on it.

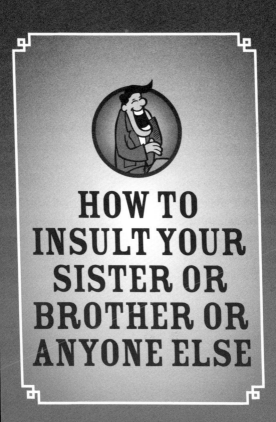

HOW TO INSULT YOUR SISTER OR BROTHER OR ANYONE ELSE

The wheel is spinning, but the hamster's asleep.

He's not the brightest crayon in the box.

She's a few clowns short of a circus.

The lights are on, but nobody's home.

She doesn't have all her dogs on one leash.

He's proof that evolution can go in reverse.

The elevator doesn't go all the way to the top.

The oven's on, but nothing's cooking.

He has delusions of adequacy.

She's not the sharpest knife in the drawer.

He's not the sharpest tool in the shed.

She's not the brightest bulb on the Christmas tree.

He fell out of the stupid tree and hit all the branches on the way down.

She's a few sandwiches
short of a picnic.

He's a few grapes short of
a bunch.

The butter has slipped off
her pancake.

He's a few fries short of a
Happy Meal.

If she had another brain it
would be lonely.

If you gave him a penny for his thoughts, you'd get change.

When she worked in a pet store, people kept asking how big she'd get.

He's so unpopular, his yo-yo never came back.

He's as bright as the North Pole in January.

She fell out of the family tree.

PRANK SQUAD

WHOOPEE CUSHION: Buy a whoopee cushion from a joke shop. Blow some air
into it. Before your victim arrives
on the scene, place the cushion
under the cushion of a couch. Try to
keep a "poker face" when the person
sits down and begins to make music.
(You can also hide nearby and operate the cushion yourself, with your
armpit.)

SOLO SOCK: Add a sock to somebody's
laundry basket. They'll go nuts trying to find the mate after they do
the wash.

MORE
INSULTS!

Amanda: "Whenever I'm in the dumps,
I buy new shoes."
Jenny: "So that's where you get
them."

A bully is picking on a boy's sister. The boy runs up and pushes the bully away, saying, "Stop picking on my sister—that's my job!"

A woman gets on a bus, holding her baby. As she pays her fare, the driver says, "That's the ugliest baby I've ever seen!"

The woman finds a seat and says to the man next to her, "The driver just insulted me. I'm really upset."

"Well you go and tell him off. And don't worry, I'll hold your monkey for you."

How do you keep a nerd in suspense?
I'll tell you later.

How do you keep your dog from begging at the table?
Let him taste your cooking.

Taylor: "Here are some cookies I
baked. Take your pick."
Josh: "No, thanks. I'll use my
hammer."

Guest: "Oh, I see you have one of those
ugly pieces of modern art.
What do you call it?"
Host: "A mirror."

I never forget a face, but in your
case I'll make an exception.

He's so stupid, he worked in a bank and stole the pens.

He's so lazy, he hires other people to walk in his sleep.

He's so old, he knew Burger King when he was a prince.

He's so old, his social insurance number is three.

He's so old, Fred Flintstone's in his yearbook.

She's so old, she drove a chariot to school.

She's so old, Jurassic Park
brought back memories.

She's so old, her birth certificate
is in Roman numerals.

His teeth are like stars.
They come out at night.

Hey, why are you telling
everyone I'm such
an idiot?
*Sorry, I didn't know it was
a secret.*

Kid: "Dad, can I go ice skating on the lake?"
Father: "Wait till it gets warmer."

Patient: "Doctor, my hair is falling out. Can you give me something to keep it in?"
Doctor: "Sure. Here's a paper bag."

Taxi driver: "That loonie tip you gave me was an insult."
Passenger: "How much do you want?"
Taxi driver: "Another loonie."
Passenger: "You want me to insult you twice?"

That magician was so bad, he made the audience disappear.

There were five jerks—
do, re, fa, so and la.
What about mi?
Sorry, I forgot about you.

PRANK SQUAD

FROZEN TOOTHBRUSH: Fill a paper cup about two-thirds full with water. Put your victim's toothbrush in the cup and put them both in the freezer at least an hour before he usually brushes his teeth. At the right moment, carefully rip the paper off the ice-covered toothbrush and put it in its normal place.

SURPRISE TEST: When a friend walks into the classroom, ask if he's ready for "today's test." (Of course, you'll have to pick a day when no test is scheduled.)

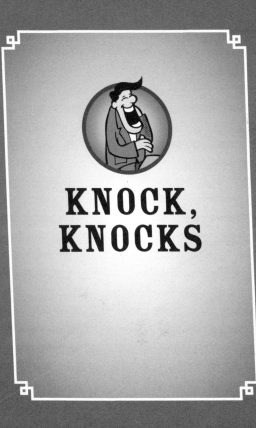

KNOCK, KNOCKS

Knock, knock.
Who's there?
Who.
Who who?
I didn't know you were an owl!

Knock, knock.
Who's there?
The interrupting cow.
The interrup—
MOOOOOO!

Knock, knock.
Who's there?
Locker.
Locker who?
Locker out, but let me in!

Knock, knock.
Who's there?
Cosmos.
Cosmos who?
Cosmos of us are waiting outside, you should let us in!

Knock, knock.
Who's there?
Apollo.
Apollo who?
Apollo-gize for not answering sooner!

Knock, knock.
Who's there?
Nobel.
Nobel who?
No bell on the door. That's why I'm knocking.

Knock, knock.
Who's there?
Izzy.
Izzy who?
Izzy home yet?

Knock, knock.
Who's there?
Denise.
Denise who?
Denise and her brother—
De nephew.

Knock, knock.
Who's there?
Atch.
Atch who?
Bless you!

Knock, knock.
Who's there?
Little old lady.
Little old lady who?
Hey—you just yodelled!

Knock, knock.
Who's there?
Howard.
Howard who?
Fine, thanks. Howard you?

Knock, knock.
Who's there?
Noah.
Noah who?
Noah good place to eat around here?

Knock, knock.
Who's there?
Avon.
Avon who?
Avon to suck your blood.

Knock, knock.
Who's there?
Voodoo.
Voodoo who?
Voodoo you think you are?

Knock, knock.
Who's there?
Banana.
Banana who?
Knock, knock.
Who's there?
Banana.
Banana who?
Knock, knock.
Who's there?
Banana.
Banana who?
Knock, knock.
Who's there?
Orange.
Orange who?
**Orange you glad I didn't
say "banana"?**

Knock, knock.
Who's there?
Police.
Police who?
Po-lice, open the door!

Knock, knock.
Who's there?
Deluxe.
Deluxe who?
Deluxe-smith. I'm here to fix de lock.

Knock, knock.
Who's there?
Anita.
Anita who?
Anita nother minute to think it over.

Knock, knock.
Who's there?
Electra.
Electra who?
Electricity. Isn't that shocking?

Knock, knock.
Who's there?
Omelette.
Omelette who?
Omelette smarter than I sound.

Will you remember me in an hour? *Yes.*
Will you remember me in a day? *Yes.*
Will you remember me in a week? *Yes.*
Will you remember me in a month? *Yes.*
Will you remember me in a year? *Yes.*
I think you won't. *Yes, I will.*
Knock, knock.
Who's there?
See? You've forgotten me already!

Knock, knock.
Who's there?
Huron.
Huron who?
**Huron my toe, could you
please step off it?**

Knock, knock.
Who's there?
Lotus.
Lotus who?
Lotus in and we'll tell you.

Knock, knock.
Who's there?
Comma.
Comma who?
**Comma little closer and
I'll kiss you.**

Knock, knock.
Who's there?
Alaska.
Alaska who?
Alask-another person if you don't know the answer.

Knock, knock.
Who's there?
Raven.
Raven who?
**Raven lunatic who wants
to knock your door down!**

Knock, knock.
Who's there?
Sparrow.
Sparrow who?
**Sparrow me the details
and let me in.**

Knock, knock.
Who's there?
Wire.
Wire who?
Wire you asking me that again? I just told you!

Knock, knock.
Who's there?
Cow go.
Cow go who?
No, cow go moo.

Knock, knock.
Who's there?
Polo.
Polo who?
Polover, you're under arrest.

Knock, knock.
Who's there?
Xena.
Xena who?
**Xena good
movie lately?**

PRANK SQUAD

BOUNCING HANKY: Place a small rubber ball in the middle of a handkerchief and fasten it with an elastic band. Then sneeze so powerfully into the hanky that it's thrust to the ground. Friends will be shocked to see the hanky bounce right back.

TIME CHANGE: Before going to bed, change all the clocks and watches in the house—except your own. Set them all an hour ahead. Then wake up at your normal time, rush into everyone's room, and tell them that they overslept. (You'll have to turn off the alarms on alarm clocks—everyone's except your own, of course.)

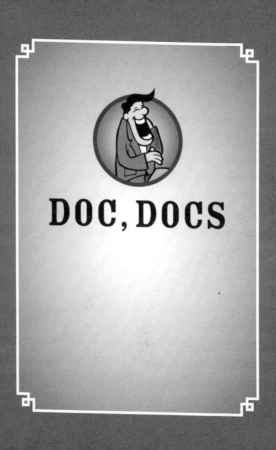

DOC, DOCS

"Doc," said the patient, "my stomach is real bad these days."

"Then send it to bed without supper," said the doctor.

"Doctor, I hurt my left hand," said the patient. "Will I be able to play the clarinet?"

"Your hand will heal in a few days," said the doctor. "So I would say you'll definitely be able to play the clarinet."

"Great!" said the patient. "Because I've always wanted to play the clarinet."

"I have pimples all over my body!" said the patient to his doctor.

"Is there anything else?" asked the doctor.

"No," said the patient. "That zit."

"I've swallowed a clock!" yells the patient to her doctor. "Please help me. I feel tick to my stomach."

A dermatologist says to her patient, "Look, I have a diagnosis for you: You've got tropical toe rash."

The patient says, "Well, I want a second opinion."

"Okay," says the dermatologist. "You're ugly too."

A doctor says to his patient, "Well, I've got good news and bad news. The bad news is, you've got a month to live."

"What? That's awful!" says the patient. "What's the good news?"

The doctor says, "I just won the lottery!"

A man goes to the doctor and says, "I've got a problem, Doc. Sometimes I think I'm a teepee and sometimes I think I'm a wigwam. Teepee, wigwam, wigwam, teepee. I need help!"

"I know what your problem is!" says the doctor. "You're too tents!"

A woman went to visit an optometrist. "Doctor," the woman said, "I think I'm suffering from poor eyesight."

"Oh, don't worry," said the doctor. "I can just print your bill bigger."

A man went to the psychiatrist and said, "Please help me, Doc. I think I'm lucky."

The doctor said, "Well, what's wrong with being lucky?"

"Lucky's my cat."

A nurse says to a recovering patient, "You're a very lucky man. The doctor took a gallstone the size of a golf ball out of you."

The patient says, "My goodness. I'd like to thank her. Is she around?"

The nurse says, "No, she thought she'd go golfing."

A patient says to his doctor, "I think my throat is wurst."

The doctor says to him, "Ahem— I think you mean 'worse.'"

"No," said the patient. "I mean wurst. Do you know how much it hurts to choke on a sausage?"

A patient says to his doctor, "I think my tonsils need to be taken out."

The doctor says, "I'll make reservations. Would they prefer dinner or dancing?"

A patient says to his doctor, "I've thrown my back out again. What should I do?"

The doctor says, "Look through the trash before it's collected!"

A patient went in to see the doctor, and the nurse asked her some questions.

"Name?" asked the nurse.

"Sandra Brown," said the patient.

"Address?" asked the nurse.

"106 Main Street."

"Flu?" asked the nurse.

"No, I walked. It's just around the corner."

A patient went to the doctor and said, "Doctor, will you give me something for my leg?"

The doctor said, "Well, I don't need it, but I can offer a dollar if you're desperate."

A psychiatrist tells her patient, "I've got good news and bad news. The good news is, you've got a split personality."

"Are you kidding me?" says the patient. "That's the good news? What's the bad?"

The psychiatrist says, "I'm going to have to bill you twice."

A surgeon steps into the patient's room, looking glum. "I'm afraid I can't operate," he says.

"Why not?" asks the patient.

"You haven't let me read your operator's manual."

A terrified mother called 911.
"Help me!" she said.
"My son just swallowed a
fork!"

The operator told her not
to worry and that he would
send an ambulance over right
away.

"What should I do until it
arrives?" the mother asked
him.

The operator said, "Use a
spoon."

A woman called a psychiatrist and said, "Doctor, my brother thinks he's the Easter Bunny."

"How long has this been going on?" asked the doctor.

"A few years," said the woman.

"Goodness, my dear lady! Why didn't you tell anyone sooner?" asked the doctor.

"Because we needed the eggs."

A woman went to her psychiatrist and said, "Doctor, I want to talk to you about my husband. He thinks he's a refrigerator."

"That's not so bad," said the doctor. "It's a rather harmless problem."

"Well, maybe," replied the woman. "But he sleeps with his mouth open and the light keeps me awake."

A woman went to see her very busy doctor. "Doctor, Doctor!" she said. "I feel like a pack of cards."

The doctor replied, "I'll deal with you later."

Alice said she wasn't feeling well. "You'd better call me a doctor," she said to her friend.

Her friend protested, "But I'd rather call you Alice."

Steve: "I went to the eye doctor because I saw fuzzy spots in front of my eyes. The doctor gave me glasses."
Leo: "Did the glasses help?"
Steve: "Yes! I can see the spots much better now!"

Doctor: "Did you take my advice and sleep with the window open?"
Patient: "Yes."
Doctor: "Did you lose your cold?"
Patient: "And my wallet and watch."

Doctor: "I have bad news and worse news."
Patient: "What's the bad news?"
Doctor: "You have 24 hours to live."
Patient: "What's the worse news?"
Doctor: "I've been trying to call you since yesterday."

Mother: "Doctor, Doctor! My daughter thinks she's a refrigerator."
Doctor: "Don't worry, I'm sure she'll chill out."

Mother: "Doctor, Doctor! My son thinks he's a smoke detector."
Doctor: "There's no cause for alarm."

Nurse: "Doctor, there is an invisible man in the waiting room."
Doctor: "Tell him I can't see him."

Patient: "I keep thinking I'm a dog."
Psychiatrist: "Get off my couch."

Patient: "Doctor, Doctor! I keep thinking I'm a $10 bill."
Doctor: "Go shopping. The change will do you good."

Patient: "Doctor, Doctor! You've got to help me! Some mornings I wake up and think I'm Donald Duck. Other mornings I think I'm Mickey Mouse."

Doctor: "Hmm. How long have you been having these Disney spells?"

Patient: "Doctor, Doctor, I feel like a pair of curtains."

Doctor: "Then pull yourself together!"

Patient: "Doctor, Doctor, I need your help!"

Doctor: "What's the problem?"

Patient: "Every night I dream there are red, spotted, slimy, angry, hungry monsters under my bed! What on earth can I do?"

Doctor: "Call a carpenter."

Patient: "What? Why would I do that?"

Doctor: "So she can saw the legs off your bed!"

Patient: "Doctor, Doctor. I have carrots growing out of my ears."

Doctor: "How did that happen?"

Patient: "Don't have a clue. I planted tomatoes."

Patient: "Doctor, I need help. I can never remember what I just said."
Doctor: "When did you first notice this problem?"
Patient: "Notice what problem?"

Patient: "Every night my foot falls asleep."
Doctor: "What's wrong with that?"
Patient: "It snores."

Patient: "Everyone says I'm a liar."
Psychiatrist: "I find that hard to believe."

Patient: "I'm here for my heart."
Doctor: "Sorry, I don't have it."

Patient: "If the doctor can't see me now, I'm leaving."
Nurse: "Calm down. What's wrong with you?"
Patient: "I have a serious wait problem."

Patient: "What does the X-ray of my head show?"
Doctor: "Nothing."

Psychiatrist: "What can I do for you?"
Tortoise: "My problem is that I'm really shy."
Psychiatrist: "Don't worry—I'll soon have you out of your shell."

Psychiatrist: "What's the problem?"
Patient: "I prefer patterned underwear to plain underwear."
Psychiatrist: "There's nothing
wrong with that. I also prefer
patterned underwear."
Patient: "So how do you like them,
baked or fried?"

Psychiatrist: "What's the
problem?"
Patient: "I think I'm a cat."
Psychiatrist: "How long has
this been going on?"
Patient: "Ever since I was a
kitten."

Surgeon: "Nurse, did you put the patient to sleep?"
Nurse: "Yeah, I just told her some of your jokes."

The dentist took one look at Billy's mouth and said, "That's the biggest cavity I've ever seen. That's the biggest cavity I've ever seen."

Billy looked at him and said, "I heard you, Doc. You don't have to repeat yourself."

"I didn't. That was an echo."

What two letters of the alphabet spell big trouble for your teeth?
D, K.

When do doctors get angry?
When they run out of patients.

Why did the clown go to the doctor?
He was feeling a little funny.

Why did the doctor go to work for the phone company?
He wanted to be an operator.

Why did the doctor keep operating on patients even though he wasn't very good at it? He needed the practice.

Why did the ham go see a doctor?
It wanted to know if it could be cured.

Why did the pie crust go to the dentist?
It needed a filling.

Why wouldn't anybody go to the duck doctor?
They all knew he was a quack.

PRANK SQUAD

ROOM SWITCH: While your friend (or brother or sister) is away, rearrange the furniture in their room. Remove posters from the walls and attach them to the ceiling. Change the position of the desk and chair. Move clothes from the closet to the drawer. Get the victim's parents' permission before you begin—and you may want to recruit other friends to help move stuff around.

YESTERDAY'S NEWS: Get the newspaper before anyone else does. Carefully replace some of the pages with the same pages of yesterday's paper. It's sure to make life confusing.

ANIMAL
QUACKERS

Rooster: "Wow, did you hear the voice on that little chick?"
Hen: "That's what you call beginner's cluck."

Two ants wandered into a large-screen TV. After crawling around for hours and hours the first ant started to cry. "I think we're lost! We'll never get out!"

"Don't worry," said the second ant. "I brought along a TV guide."

What did the owl do when her owner abandoned her?
Nothing. She didn't give a hoot.

What do pigs see when they go to the ballet?
Swine Lake.

What do rabbits sing to each other once a year?
"Hoppy Birthday."

What do you give to an injured pig?
Oinkment.

What should you do when someone throws a goose at you?
Duck.

What do you say when someone throws a duck at a duck?
"Duck, duck!"

What do you say when someone throws a goose at a duck?
"Duck, duck, goose!"

What does a duck have before bedtime?
Milk and quackers.

What does the cow like to do on her day off?
Go to the moovies.

What happened when the pig couldn't get up from his fall?
He called a ham-bulance.

Where did he go to recover from his fall?
The hog-spital.

What is a frog's favourite pop?
Croaka-Cola.

What kind of horse makes you wake up scared?
A nightmare.

What sound does a chicken crossed with a cow make?
Cock-a-doodle-moo.

What's the dumbest name for a zebra?
Spot.

What's the easiest way to count a herd of cattle?
Use a cow-culator.

What's worse than a giraffe with a sore throat?
A hippopotamus with chapped lips.

What's worse than a hippopotamus with chapped lips?
A centipede with athlete's foot.

Where can you find out more about ducks?
In a duck-tionary.

Where did the sheep go after high school?
Ewe-niversity.

Where do baby calves go for lunch?
The calf-eteria.

Who's a lamb's favourite superhero?
B-a-a-atman.

Why are pigs always in fashion?
They're sty-lish.

Why did the duck become a spy?
He was good at quacking codes.

Why did the farmer give the cow a hammer at bedtime?
Because he wanted the cow to hit the hay.

Why did the teacher send the duck out of the classroom?
He was making wise quacks.

Why didn't the turkey finish his dinner?
He was already stuffed.

Why do cows have bells?
Because their horns don't work.

Why do kings have royal seals?
Because royal walruses eat too much.

Why should you be careful when playing against a team of big cats?
They might be cheetahs.

Why was the chicken team so bad at baseball?
They kept hitting fowl balls.

Why was the little boy afraid of the turkey?
He heard it was a gobblin.

Why was the rabbit so unhappy?
She was having a bad hare day.

Why won't banks allow kangaroos to open accounts?
Their cheques always bounce.

What's the name of the best-selling biography of 400 famous owls?
Who's Who.

Baby snake: "Mom, are we poisonous?"
Mom snake: "We most certainly are! Why?"
Baby snake: "I just bit my tongue!"

A woman opens her front door one morning to find a snail sitting on her doorstep. She swings her leg back and kicks the snail all the way down the walkway in front of her house. Two years later, the doorbell rings. When the woman answers the door, she looks down and there is the snail, who asks, "What was *that* all about?"

A leopard went to see an eye doctor because he thought he needed a checkup. "What's wrong?" asked the doctor.

"Well, Doctor," said the leopard, "every time I look at my wife, I see spots before my eyes."

"What's wrong with that?" asked the doctor. "You are a leopard."

"What's that got to do with anything?" asked the leopard. "My wife's a zebra."

PRANK SQUAD

SNOOP TRAP: Put a big poster on your wall that reads, NOSY! Then tape a Do Not Enter sign on your door and leave your room. Your curious brother (or sister, or parent) will be caught in the act.

MESSY DRINK: Take a cardboard cup and prick some holes just below the rim. Pour water in the cup, but make sure it's below the level of the holes. As your friend picks up the cup, the drink will sprinkle out.

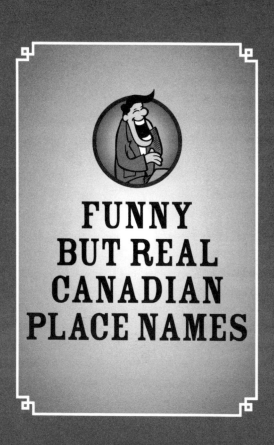

FUNNY
BUT REAL
CANADIAN
PLACE NAMES

Blow Me Down,
Newfoundland and Labrador

Goobies,
Newfoundland and Labrador

Tickle Cove,
Newfoundland and Labrador

Jerry's Nose,
Newfoundland and Labrador

Poopoo Creek, British Columbia

Ecum Secum, Nova Scotia

Poodiac, New Brunswick

Sissiboo Falls, Nova Scotia

Crapaud, Prince Edward Island

Saint-Louis-du-Ha-Ha!, Quebec

Bummers Roost, Ontario

Finger, Manitoba

Nut Mountain, Saskatchewan

Stand Off, Alberta

Spuzzum, British Columbia

Joe Batt's Arm, Newfoundland and Labrador

Billy Butts Pond, Newfoundland and Labrador

Mushaboom, Nova Scotia

Punkeydoodles Corners, Ontario

Wawa, Ontario

Community Punch Bowl, Alberta

Yak, British Columbia

Skookumchuck, British Columbia

Tuktoyaktuk, Northwest Territories

PRANK SQUAD

APRIL FOOL'S DAY CALLS: Leave the following message for someone: "Mr. Lyon (or Ellie Phant, or G. Raph) would like you to call him back." Include the phone number of the local zoo. This is a very common joke, and many zoos are actually prepared for it and will ask the caller to make a donation.

FLOUR HEAD: Place a bag with a little flour on it on the top of a slightly open door. When the victim opens the door to walk through, the bag will fall and cover his or her hair with the white powdery stuff.

DID YOU HEAR WHAT THEY SAID?

What did Huey, Dewey and Louie say when something was falling on their uncle's head?
"Donald—duck!"

What did one elevator say to the other?
"I think I'm coming down with something!"

What did one flea say to the other flea as they were leaving to go to the movies?
"Shall we walk or take a dog?"

What did one plate say to the other?
"Dinner's on me."

What did one skeleton say to the other?
"If we had any guts, we'd get out of here."

What did one wall say to the other?
"Meet me at the corner."

What did the alien say to the eggs?
"Take me to your beater."

What did the alien say to the tabby cat?
"Take me to your litter."

What did the alien say when his spaceship landed at Taco Bell?
"Take me to the big enchilada."

What did the alien say to the tree?
"Take me to your cedar."

What did the bald man say when he got a comb for his birthday?
"I'll never part with it."

What did the big clock say to his shy son?
"Take your hands off your face."

What did the broom say to the dustpan?
"Let's make a clean sweep."

What did the budgie say when it was hungry?
"Long time, no seed."

What did the carpet say to the floor?
"Don't move, I've got you covered."

What did the computer keyboard say to the typist?
"You're really pushing my buttons!"

What did the couch say halfway through the marathon?
"Sofa, so good."

What did the cucumber say to the vinegar?
"Well, this is a fine pickle you've gotten us into!"

What did the pickle say at the poker game?
"Dill me in."

What did the drummer say when his band teacher told him he had no rhythm?
"That's because I'm beat."

What did the farmer say when she fell in the haystack?
"Somebody bale me out!"

What did the fisherman say to the magician?
"Pick a cod, any cod."

What did the fly say to the flypaper?
"I'm stuck on you."

What did the grape say when the rhinoceros trampled it?
Not much. It just let out a little wine.

What did the mama melon say to her daughter when the girl wanted to run away and marry her boyfriend?
"You cantaloupe."

What did the milk say to the blender?
"I'm all shook up."

What did the milkmaid say to the impatient butter?
"You'll have to wait your churn."

What did the mother kangaroo say when her baby was kidnapped?
"Somebody help me catch that pickpocket!"

What did the mouse say to the webcam?
"Cheese!"

What did the ocean say to the shore?
"Glad to sea you!"

What did the ocean say to the shore?
Nothing, it just waved.

What did the pig say when he fell down the stairs?
"Oh, my achin' bacon."

What did the refrigerator say to the milk?
"Now, don't get fresh with me."

What did the rope say after it tangled?
"Oh no, knot again!"

What did the sheep say to his fiancée?
"There's something I have to tell you: I love ewe."

What did the sink say to the dirty dishes?
"You're in hot water now!"

What did the soda say to the bottle opener?
"Hey, can you help me find my pop?"

What did the sun say when it was introduced to Earth?
"Pleased to heat you."

What did the tailor say after his client fired him?
"Suit yourself."

What did the tomato dad say to his tomato son who was lagging behind?
"Ketchup!"

What did the cookie say to the melon?
Nothing. Cookies can't talk, silly!

Barry: "Did you hear about the turtle on the highway?"
Larry: "What was he doing on it?"
Barry: "Oh, about two kilometres an hour."

Cate: "Did you hear about the three French cats—Un, Deux and Trois?"
Johnnie: "No. What happened?"
Cate: "They were on a boat that tipped over. It was very sad. Un, Deux, Trois, quatre cinq."

Did you hear about the butcher who backed up?

He got a little behind in his work.

Did you hear about the crimes over at that house they're renovating?
The shower was stalled while the curtains were held up. I heard the window was framed for it.

Did you hear about the delivery van loaded with thesauruses that crashed into a taxi?
Witnesses were astounded, shocked, taken aback, surprised, startled, dumbfounded, thunderstruck and caught unawares.

Did you hear about the dentist and the manicurist?
They fought tooth and nail.

Did you hear about the farmer arrested for selling rotten fruit?
He was judged by his pears.

Did you hear about the ice that lost its job?
It was crushed.

Did you hear about the jigsaw puzzle that got fired?
It went to pieces.

Did you hear about the kid who planted lots of seeds on his neighbours' lawns?
He wanted to live on De Grassi Street.

Did you hear about the pig that learned karate?
He's now doing pork chops.

Did you hear about the poor vampire slayer?

He tried to kill a vampire by driving a pork chop through its heart because steaks were too expensive.

Did you hear about the two mindreaders who met on the street?
The first one said, "Well, you're fine. How am I?"

Did you hear about the undertaker who buried a person in the wrong place?
It was a grave error.

Did you hear about the underwear that lost its job?
It was bummed.

Did you hear about the wizard who became a film director?
He really made movie magic.

Did you hear how hard it is to get a job as a sword-swallower? There's cutthroat competition.

Did you hear that joke about the fart?
It really stinks.

Did you hear that the fire-eater got engaged?
He ran into an old flame.

**Did you hear the one about
the compulsive-liar
sandwich?**
It was full of baloney.

**Did you hear the one about the
knives?**
It's a cut-up.

**Did you hear the one about the
lion who ate clowns?**
You'll roar.

**Did you hear the one about
the mummies?**
*Too bad, it wrapped
already.*

Did you hear the one about the vampire?
It was a vein attempt at humour.

Did you hear the rumour about the dinosaur that terrorized Florida?
It was a croc.

PRANK SQUAD

UNATTAINABLE PRIZE: Send an anonymous letter—but the second page only. Page 2 can start with something such as: "So please claim your prize by following the instructions on the previous page."

GOLDFISH SNACK: Know somebody who has a goldfish? Get a carrot and carve a piece in the shape of a goldfish tail. When you visit your victim, hide the carrot piece in your pocket. As you look at the goldfish, say how hungry you are. When the person turns around, quietly place the carrot in your mouth, with the "tail" hanging out. Then mumble something, and when the person turns to you, start to chew the carrot "tail" and then swallow it. Yum.

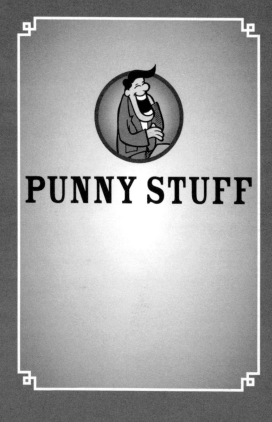

PUNNY STUFF

Mary's husband, Bill, lost his job as a tailor in a local shop, but he didn't talk much about it or seem too bothered. Mary was so curious that she finally asked, "Why is it that you're not working as a tailor anymore, Bill?"

Bill thought a moment and then said, "Well, I guess it didn't really suit me. It was a sew-sew job."

My friend sent me 20 different puns. He hoped that at least one of the puns would make me laugh. No pun in 10 did.

A boiled egg is hard to beat.

A wildcat committed a horrible
murder and then left the country.
The police came upon the scene
of the crime and were stumped.
They found the paw prints and the
broken lock but were unable to
catch the crook. How come?
They couldn't find the missing lynx.

A duck walks into a drugstore
and asks for a tube of lipstick.
The cashier says, "That'll
be $4.99." The duck replies,
"Just put it on my bill."

A farmer went out to the barn to milk his cow early in the morning. He was milking away quietly and had the bucket almost half full when a bug flew into the barn and started circling his head. Suddenly, the bug flew into the cow's ear. The farmer didn't think much about it until the bug squirted out into his bucket. Looks like it went in one ear and out the udder.

Boy, things are expensive. I just bought a winter coat. Even down is up.

A lion had to appear at the courthouse to prove he had been a good ruler of the animal kingdom. He was nervous about his first day in court, but his friends told him he'd be all right if he just focused on the questions the judge asked and answered them as best he could.

The lion dressed up in his very best suit and got to court right on time. He smiled at the judge and was very polite. He was a little shocked when the judge asked him, "Are you a lion?"

"No, madam," stammered the lion. "I swear, I'm telling the truth!"

A little boy swallowed some coins and was taken to the hospital. When his brother called to see how he was doing, the nurse said, "No change yet."

A snail goes into a car dealership. She asks the salesperson if they sell red convertibles.

The salesperson answers, "Yes. But do you have a proper licence?"

The snail replies, "Yes, but the thing is, I'll buy the car on one condition—that you have a big *S* painted on each side."

The salesperson thinks about it and agrees to do so. A few weeks later, the car is ready, and the salesperson calls the snail to tell her she can come pick it up. The snail is pleased with her car. The salesperson is still wondering about the reason for the paint job and asks, "So why did you want an *S* painted on each side of the car?"

The snail replies, "When I drive by, I want everyone to say, 'Look at that *S* car go!'"

What became of Beethoven after he died?
He became a decomposer.

Sheila was called into her teacher's office for a talk.

"I'm sorry," said the teacher, "but I found out you cheated on your test, so I'm changing your A to an F. Do you have anything to say?"

"Yes," said Sheila. "That's pretty degrading."

Boy: "Why didn't you pull a rabbit out of your hat?"
Magician: "Because I just washed my hare and I can't get it to do anything now!"

What did the dog do after he swallowed a firefly?
He barked with de-light.

What do computers eat when they get hungry?
Chips.
How?
They take mega-bytes.

What do you call it when a bull swallows a stick of dynamite?
A-bomb-in-a-bull.

What do you get when you cross Cinderella with a rabbit?
A hare ball.

What do you get when you cross a bunny rabbit with the World Wide Web?
A hare Net.

What do you get when you cross a cow with a volcano?
Udder disaster.

What kind of hat does Sir Lancelot wear?
A knight cap.

What's Moby Dick's favourite dinner?
Fish 'n' ships.

When a clock is hungry, it goes back four seconds.

Who made the plans for Noah's Ark?
An Ark-i-tect.

Who was the roundest knight at King Arthur's Court?
Sir Cumference.

Boy: "I'll stop being frightened if you'll stop being scared."
Girl: "That sounds like a fear trade to me."

Why are some school classes not very interesting?
Because they were developed by the Bored of Education.

Why can't a bicycle stand alone?
Because it is two tired.

Why couldn't the bell keep a secret?
It always tolled.

Why do dragons sleep all day?
So they can fly knights.

Why was the mushroom the hit of the party?
He was a fungi.

Would Little Miss Muffet share her curds?
No whey.

Writing with a broken pencil is pointless.

PRANK SQUAD

FAKE BOOGER: Stick a little sauerkraut in one of your nostrils. It's sure to gross someone out when you fake a sneeze.

SAUSAGE FINGER: Get a small, skinny sausage that's roughly the same colour as your skin. Trim the sausage carefully so that it looks like a finger. Then, just before you see your victim, squeeze the sausage between two of your fingers. At the right moment, put out your hand for the person to shake it. Shake hands, then pull your hand away—leaving the "finger" in the person's grip. Eww.

HOW DO
THEY DO IT?

How do astronauts take their kids to school?
In space-station wagons.

How do bears walk around?
With bear feet.

How do corn kernels propose marriage?
They pop the question.

How do gymnasts feel after a routine?
Head over heels.

How do astronauts hold up their pants?
With asteroid belts.

How do the three men in the tub sign their love letters?
"I lub-a-dub-dub you."

How do you brush a sabre-toothed tiger's teeth?
Very carefully.

How do you carve wood?
Whittle by whittle.

How do you catch a per-cussionist who's on the run?
With a snare drum.

How do you catch a rabbit?
Hide behind a tree and make carrot noises.

How do you catch a squirrel?
Climb a tree and act like a nut.

How do you compare the speeds of two computers?
Push them off the top of a building at the same time, and see which one hits the ground first.

How do you find a spider on the Internet?
Check out its website.

How do you fire a math teacher?
Tell her she's history.

How do you get an astronaut's baby to fall asleep?
Rocket.

**How do you
know when
you're talking to
a mad scientist
and her clone?**
They they say
say everything
everything
twice twice.

**How do you know when
your older sister's an
alien?**
*She always knocks before
coming into your room.*

How do you learn to be a judge?
Mostly through trial and error.

How do you make a bandstand?
Take away their chairs.

How do you make a casserole?
Put it on a skateboard.

How do you make a puppy disappear?
Use Spot remover.

How do you make antifreeze?
Take away her blanket.

How do you make meat loaf?
Send it on a holiday.

How do you make seven even?
Remove the s.

How do you say pickle in Spanish?
Pickle in Spanish.

How do you throw the best party in the universe?
Planet.

How do you toast a sheep?
"Here's to ewe."

How do you turn a regular scientist into a mad scientist?
Step on her toes.

How does a mouse feel after it takes a bath?
Squeaky clean.

How does a skeleton prepare for a test?
It bones up.

How does broccoli feel when it's been cooked?
It's steamed.

How does the man on the moon trim his hedge?
Eclipse it.

How does the snake charmer sign his letters?
"Love and hisses."

What is everyone in the world doing at the same time?
Growing older.

PRANK
SQUAD

HIDDEN STINK: Don't play this joke if there's a pet around the house. Hide something smelly in your victim's room. It can be a piece of cheese, placed inside a container. The smell will grow after several days. Just make sure you quietly remove the cheese before the smell gets too disgusting.

FRUIT FAKE-OUT: Convince your parents that their plants are growing fruit way out of season. Buy some beautiful, ripe pieces of fruit and twist-tie them to the vines or branches.

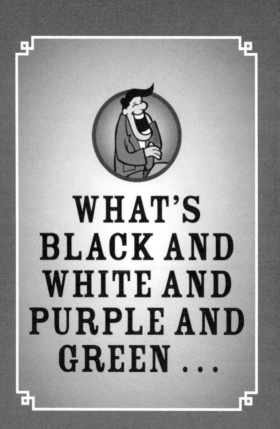

WHAT'S BLACK AND WHITE AND PURPLE AND GREEN ...

What's black and white and flat?
A panda that's been run over.

What's black and white and green and black and white?
Two zebras fighting over a pickle.

What's black and white and red all over?
A newspaper.

What else is black and white and red all over?
A zebra with a sunburn.

What's green and sings?
Elvis Parsley.

What's purple and surrounded by water?
Grape Britain.

What's small, round and blue?
A cranberry holding its breath.

What does purple do when it gets angry?
It sees red.

What's red and goes "ding dong"?
I don't know—what?
A red ding dong.
What's blue and goes "ding dong"?
A blue ding dong?
Right!
What's green and goes "ding dong"?
A green ding dong?
Right again.
Now, what's purple and goes "ding dong"?
Well, that must be a purple ding dong.
Correct. And what's pink and goes "ding dong"?
A pink ding dong?
Nope. They don't come in pink.

What Greek king was purple and conquered the ancient world? Alexander the Grape.

What is brown and sticky? *A stick.*

What's big and white and lives on Mars?
A Martian-mallow.

Why isn't red happy to see purple?
It starts to feel blue.

PRANK SQUAD

PRE-SLICED BANANA: This joke is a long-time favourite. In addition to a banana, you'll need a sterilized needle. (Recruit an accomplice—an adult who'll help you prepare the needle.) Use the needle to pierce the top part of the banana skin. Move the needle from side to side—this will slice the banana. Remove the needle, and again stick it in the banana, a little farther down this time, directly below the first hole. Repeat the action, working your way down to the bottom of the banana. Your friend will be surprised—to say the least—when he peels the banana and discovers that it's already been sliced.

HOCKEY
HUMOUR

Did you hear about the guy who went to a fight?
A hockey game broke out.

Did you hear about the hockey player in the new horror movie?
He plays a ghoulie.

Hockey is 75 percent mental.
The other half is physical.

Hockey players have been complaining about violence for a long time. Unfortunately, without any teeth, nobody can understand them.

I think hockey's a great game. Of course, my father is a dentist.

I wondered why the puck was getting bigger. Then it hit me.

Jamie arrived home after his hockey game. "How'd you do?" asked his father.

"You aren't going to believe it, Dad," Jamie shouted. "I was responsible for the winning goal."

"That's great," said his dad. "How did you do that?"

"I missed my check on the other team's top scorer."

**Reporter to hockey player: "Did
you ever break your nose?"
Hockey player to reporter: "No, but
five other players did."**

**John: "Did anyone laugh when you
fell on the ice?"
Brad: "No, but the ice made some
terrible cracks."**

The daughter of a famous hockey
star was watching television, and her
grandmother was in the other room.
"Grandma, come here! Dad's on the
television again!" yelled the little girl.

Her grandma yelled back, "You
just tell your father to get off the
television and sit on the couch like a
normal adult."

They named their kid Later because teams are always trading for a player to be named later.

What has 12 legs and goes crunch, crunch, crunch?
A hockey team eating potato chips.

What's the difference between a hockey player and a dog?
The hockey player wears a team uniform, the dog just pants.

What did Bugs Bunny say to Sidney Crosby?
"Eh . . . what's up, jock?"

What would you get if you crossed a great hockey player with a Sea-Doo?

Wayne Jet-Ski.

What do you get when you cross a hockey player with a cow?
The team Jersey.

Why do hockey players wear numbers?
Because their bodies can't always be identified with dental records.

Why did the disk drive become a professional goalie? It kept making great saves.

Boy at hockey arena, returning to his seat: "Excuse me, sir, did I step on your foot a little while ago?"

Annoyed man: "Yes, as a matter of fact you did."

Boy: "Oh, good. Then this is my row."

While walking along the street, a man saw a man and a dog sitting beside a sign that said, "Talking Dog for Sale, $10." The man couldn't believe his ears when the dog said, "Please buy me. I'm a great dog. I played professional hockey. I was even nominated most valuable player."

"That dog really does talk!" the man gasped. "Why in the world do you want to sell him for only 10 dollars?"

"He never played professional hockey," said the dog's owner, "and I can't stand liars."

Why were the charges against the hockey team dropped?
They had a strong defence.

What's black and white and never right?
A hockey referee.

What's the best hockey team in the universe?
The All-Stars.

What does Scrooge wear when he plays hockey?
Cheap skates.

When did cave people invent hockey?
During the ice age.

A woman goes ice fishing. She takes out an ice pick and begins to hack away. She hears a loud voice from above saying, "There're no fish there." She goes to another spot and starts to pick away. Again comes the voice: "There're no fish there either." She tries a third spot. Once more, she hears the voice from above. "Nope. Not there either."

Finally, the woman, growing a little nervous, looks up and asks, "Are you God?"

The response from above booms, "No. I'm the arena manager."

Alex: "Can you skate?"
Tom: "I don't know. I've never been able to stand up long enough to find out."

Definition of a puck: A hard rubber disc that hockey players hit when they aren't hitting each other.

Why did the hockey player tear off his clothes after he scored a goal? He wanted his team to have a winning streak.

PRANK SQUAD

MEDICINE CABINET SURPRISE: If you think you have a nosy visitor, fill the medicine cabinet with table tennis balls. Won't your guest be surprised when he or she opens the cabinet door!

ENDLESS THREAD: Take a spool of thread the same colour as your shirt, jacket or pants. Hide the spool in a sleeve or under the waist of your pants. Let a bit of the thread hang free so that your mother will notice it. When she tries to pull off the bit of thread, it will roll off the spool endlessly. Act just as surprised as your mom.

MORE GOOD
SPORTS

Do old bikers ever die?
No, they just get re-cycled.

**Girl: "Coach, why does that guy look
so mad when he runs a marathon?"
Coach: "He's a cross-country runner."**

How come the football player didn't score a touchdown?
His flight was stuck in a holding pattern.

Two old men, Moe and Sam, have been friends forever. Sam is dying, so Moe comes to visit. "Sam," says Moe. "You know how we both love baseball. Somehow, when you go, you've got to tell me if there's baseball in heaven." Sam agrees, and moments later he passes on.

It's midnight a couple of nights later. Moe is in bed, when a distant voice calls out to him, "Moe. . . ."

"Who is it?" says Moe, sitting up suddenly.

"It's Sam."

"Sam? Where are you?"

"I'm in heaven, and I've got good news and bad news."

"Tell me the good news first," says Moe.

"The good news," says Sam, "is that there is baseball in heaven."

"That's wonderful," says Moe. "What's the bad news?"

"You're pitching Tuesday!"

How do you stop bacon from curling in the frying pan?
Take away their brooms.

Little league coach: "What would you do if it was the bottom of the ninth with two outs and three runners on base?"
Relief pitcher: "Come out of the dugout so I could see the action better!"

What do baseball players give their fiancées?
Diamonds.

What do you get when you cross a baseball pitcher with a carpet?
A throw rug.

What do you get when you cross a baseball player with a monster?
A double-header.

What do you get when you cross a basketball team with crullers?
Dunkin' doughnuts.

Are baseball umpires good eaters?
Yes—they always clean their plates.

What do you get when you cross a golfer with a library?
Book clubs.

What game does Godzilla like best?
Squash.

What has four wheels and grows on a vine?
A skategourd.

What job did Dracula Junior have at the baseball stadium?
He was the bat boy for night games.

What kind of match doesn't light on fire?
A tennis match.

What kind of player gives refunds?
A quarterback.

What position does a pig play in football?
Swinebacker.

What's a diver's favourite game?
Pool.

What's a good place to take your golf clubs after the game?
A tee party.

What's the best thing to drink during a marathon?
Running water.

When do ballplayers get emotional?
When they choke up on the bat.

Where do baseball pitchers learn new pitches?
They look in the en-strike-lopedia.

Where do hair colourists sit when they go to baseball games?
In the bleachers.

Who's a better boxer, a bean or a chicken?
The bean—he's no chicken.

Who's young and perky and attacks sports officials?
Buffy the Umpire Slayer.

Why are a golfer's pants never wrinkled?
Because golfers use nine-irons.

Why did the athlete take up bowling?
She thought it would be up her alley.

Why did the baseball player take her bat to the library?
Her teacher told her to hit the books.

Why did the elastic band go to the baseball game?
It wanted to enjoy the seventh-inning stretch.

Why did the golfer bring two pairs of socks to the tournament?
In case she got a hole in one.

Why did the kangaroo lose the basketball game?
He ran out of bounds.

Why did the pitcher bring an old pocket watch to his games?
So he could wind up before throwing the ball.

Why do scientists love baseball? They love looking at slides.

Why do soccer players do well in school?
Because they use their heads.

Why does it take longer to run from second base to third base than it does to run from first to second?
Because there's a shortstop between second and third.

Why don't eggs make good quarterbacks?
When their defence cracks, they're too quick to scramble.

Why don't matches play baseball?
One strike and they're out.

Why is it a good idea to have a frog on your baseball team?
They're good at catching pop flies.

Why did the football player follow the other team's linebacker?

Because the grass is always greener on the other side of de-fence.

Why was the prizefighter fired from his job?

He was always punching out early.

PRANK SQUAD

TOY TOOLBOX: Fill your dad's toolbox with toy tools.

• • • • •

PHONE GAG: Phone jokes aren't as popular as they once were, now that the caller's number is easy to see or to trace. But here's one to try if you think you won't be caught. Phone someone, and ask to speak to George (or any other name). When they tell you it's the wrong number, hang up. Later, have a friend call the same number, again asking for George. Have another friend phone a little later, also asking for George. Then call the number one last time and say, "Hi. This is George. Have there been any messages?"

YOU WON'T
FIND THESE
IN THE
LIBRARY

Cheap Imitation by Harley Worthit

Crazy Stuff to Do by Ima Loony

Fibbing All the Time by Liza Lott

The Art of Shaving by Harry Mann

Over the Cliff by Hugo Furst

The German Bank Robbery by Hans Upp

The Cat's Cover-up by Kitty Litter

Monsters at Large by Frank N. Stein

Under the Bleachers by Seymour Butz

Late Again by Misty Bus

My Favourite Valentine by Bea Mine

My Life in the Crazy House by I.M. Nutty

Not Enough Jokes by Annie Moore

Striking it Rich by Jack Potts

Revenge of the Lion by Claude Bottom

Crime Doesn't Pay by Laura Norder

Moving Day by Ivor Newhouse

The Tornado by Major D. Saster

We're Soaked! by Rufus Leeking

Sounds in the Night by Al Lee Katz

Mad Dash to the Outhouse by Willie Makitt and Betty Kant

PRANK SQUAD

PSYCH-OUT PITCHER: When you're having dinner, keep an empty pitcher on the table. (To keep the victim from seeing inside, use a pitcher that's made from something other than glass or clear plastic.) When somebody asks you to pass the pitcher, pick it up as though it's full and heavy, then place it next to the person. They'll think it weighs a lot and will use a fair bit of strength to lift it. Their reaction should be pretty funny.

DRY-BREAD DARE: Bet a friend that he can't eat a slice of dry bread in less than a minute. There can't be anything on the bread, and your friend can't drink anything either. It's more difficult than it sounds—and even if your friend can do it, it's fun to watch him take the challenge.

DINOSAURS
AND OTHER
OLDIES

An old man got up every morning at six o'clock to sprinkle white powder in his front and back yards. One morning his paper boy asked him: "Why are you always putting powder around your house?"

"To keep the dinosaurs away," replied the old man.

"But there aren't any dinosaurs left," said the boy.

"Well, then, it worked!" said the old man.

How do you know if there's a triceratops under your bed?
You listen for a dino-snore.

How do you know there's a brontosaurus in the house?
The cheese is missing from the mousetraps.

How do you know there's a tyrannosaurus in the house?
The brontosaurus is missing.

How do you know when a dinosaur has gone bad?
Check its expiration date.

If a triceratops and a pebble are standing on the edge of a cliff, which one jumps first? The pebble—it's a little boulder.

A stegosaurus decided to go for a walk. The stegosaurus walked up a mountain, down a road and through a valley. At one end of the valley, it met another stegosaurus.

The other stegosaurus wanted some company, so it followed the first stegosaurus back across the valley, up the road and down the other side of the mountain. There they met a third stegosaurus. The third stegosaurus was also lonely, so it followed the other two stegosauruses. All three stegosauruses headed off together and walked back up the small hill and through the other valley. This time they took a right turn and headed down a new road, which ended in a forest. There they met another stegosaurus having lunch.

What did the stegosaurus say when it saw the other three?

Nothing. Stegosauruses can't talk.

What did the stegosaurus say to the cute brontosaurus at the tar pit?
"Hey, I'm glad you decided to stick around."

What do you call it when a tyrannosaurus throws a brontosaurus at another tyrannosaurus?
Food fight!

What do you get when you cross a prehistoric animal with a cat?
A 'saur-puss.

What do you get when you turn a dinosaur upside down?
A triceratops-y turvy.

What does a triceratops sit on?
Its tricera-bottom.

What is a T. rex's favourite number?
Eight.

What kind of material do dinosaurs use for the floors of their homes?
Rep-tiles.

What music do hip dinosaurs listen to?
Raptor music.

What would you get if you crossed a dinosaur with a pig?
Jurassic Pork.

What's louder than a dinosaur?
A whole bunch of dinosaurs.

What's the difference between a pterodactyl and a chicken?
When you come down with a cold, nobody ever offers you a bowl of hot pterodactyl soup.

What's the difference between a pterodactyl and a parrot?
You'd know the answer if you ever let a pterodactyl sit on your shoulder.

What's the difference between a pterodactyl and a turkey?
The drumsticks are bigger on a pterodactyl.

Where does the dodo bird like to fly for his winter vacation?
Nowhere—dodos can't fly.

Where does Tyrannosaurus rex live?
Anywhere it wants to.

Where do pterodactyls leave their cars?
In Jurassic parking lots.

Which dinosaur put on the bandage?
The one with the dino-sore.

Which dinosaur roamed the wild, wild west?
Tyrannosaurus Tex.
And what did he ride?
A bronco-saurus.

Which dinosaur sleeps all day?
The dino-snore.

Why aren't there any dinosaurs in animal crackers?
Because they're extinct, silly! And anyway, they wouldn't fit in the box.

Why did the apatosaurus have the factory for dinner?
Because she was a plant eater.

Why did the brontosaurus climb into the active volcano?
He wasn't very smart.

Why did the dinosaurs become extinct?
Because they wouldn't take a bath.

William says to Gillian one day, "Your dad seems to get along well with your pet Tyrannosaurus rex. I guess that's because no one would want to argue with 12 tons of unstoppable fury."

Gillian says, "Hey, watch it, that's my dad you're talking about!"

PRANK SQUAD

SHORT-SHEETING: This is a prank that's been around for ages and is very popular at camp. When making a bed, fold the top sheet in half so that it goes only halfway down. Then tuck it in like you would if the sheet went all the way to the bottom. Place the blanket and pillow on top of the sheet. Everything appears normal, but when the victim stretches his legs toward the foot of the bed, he'll get a surprise.

TOILET SEAT TROUBLE: This is an old gag—and a gross one. Lift the toilet seat. Spread plastic wrap over the bowl. Replace the seat. Then wait for the next family member to use the toilet. Splash!

A LITTLE
BIT OF
EVERYTHING

How many carpenters does it take to screw in a light bulb?
Hey! That's the electrician's job!

How many jugglers does it take to screw in a light bulb?
One, but he uses at least three bulbs.

How many country musicians does it take to change a light bulb?
Five: One to change the bulb, and four to sing about how much they'll miss the old one.

What did the light bulb say to the switch? "You turn me on."

A man walked up to the window at the post office. "Any mail for Mike Howe?" he asked the clerk.

The clerk stared at him and then replied, "No. And there's nothing for your horse either."

A woman sits down in a restaurant and says to the waiter, "Waiter, I'd like an alligator, and make it snappy."

An invisible man married an invisible woman. The kids were nothing to look at.

Bart: "I feel like spaghetti."
Howard: "Funny, you don't look like spaghetti!"

Customer: "I'd like some beef, and make it lean."
Butcher: "Which way?"

Do you have a head of lettuce? Then how come your face is so green?

If you eat three-quarters of a pie, what do you have?
An angry parent.

It's that time of the year again: Will February March?
No, but April May.

Woman at hotel: "Sir, can you please call me a taxi?"
Valet: "Certainly. You are a taxi."

Older man 1: "Hey, I just bought a fantastic new hearing aid."
Older man 2: "What kind is it?"
Older man 1: "About three-thirty."

Sara: "I'm taking lessons in fishing and playing *Go Fish*."
Leslie: "That's a weird combination."
Sara: "Not really. Now I'm a reeler and a dealer."

Little girl: "I'm thirsty."
Little boy: "I'm Friday. Come over Saturday, and we'll have a sundae."

Hannah: "Would you care to join me in a cup of tea?"
Sam: "Do you really think there's enough room for the two of us?"

My grandmother started walking 10 kilometres a day when she was 60. She's 75 now— and we don't know where she is.

New shoelace: "Why are you crying, old shoelace? Can't you tie a bow?"
Old shoelace: "No, I'm a frayed knot."

One astronaut asks another astronaut if she has ever heard of the planet Saturn. The second astronaut says, "I'm not sure, but it has a familiar ring."

Passenger to pilot: "I'm really nervous. This is my first flight." Pilot: "Cool! Mine too."

Penny: "Say, Jenny, how did you get a swollen nose?"
Jenny: "I bent down to smell a brose in my garden."
Penny: "Not brose, rose. There's no *b* in rose."
Jenny: "There was in this one!"

Ryan's sister asked him what he thought about his job at the plant. "Well, it's growing on me," said Ryan.

Robbie and his friends were talking after school. "Where's your favourite place to eat a hamburger?" asked Owen.

Jimmy said he liked to sit

in the park. Sam said he liked the picnic tables at the fair.

"What about you, Robbie?" Owen asked. "Where's your favourite place to eat a hamburger?"

Robbie replied, "In my mouth."

Salesperson: "This computer will do half your job for you."
Customer: "Great—I'll take two."

Store manager: "Why do you always pick my store to rob?"
Thief: "You always advertise such great sales!"

Did you hear about the robber who stole a calendar? He got 12 months.

The washer-and-dryer salesperson says to the customer, "Have you decided on a model?"

"I'm not sure," says the customer.

The salesperson says, "That's no problem—just take it for a spin."

What are a gas station attendant's favourite shoes?
Pumps.

What are a plumber's favourite shoes?
Clogs.

What did the corn give his fiancée when he proposed?
An ear ring.

What do weathermen call their baby boys?
Sunny.

What does a millionaire make for dinner every night of the week?
Reservations.

What game do tornadoes like to play?
Twister.

What has four wheels and flies?
A garbage truck.

What has lots of eyes but can't see?
A potato.

What has one horn and gives milk?
A milk truck.

What should you do if your cake strikes out?
Call in the next batter.

What's the longest word in the world?
Smiles, because it's a mile from one s to the other.

When are farmers mean?
When they pull the ears off corn.

When do mothers have baby boys?
On Son-days.

When is a carton of milk like rain?
When it pours.

Where do butchers dance?
At the meat ball.

Who gets the most respect in the circus?
The tall man—everyone looks up to him.

Why are raspberries such bad drivers?
They're always getting into jams.

Why couldn't the monkey catch the banana?
The banana split.

Why couldn't the sailors play cards?

Because they were standing on the deck.

Why do firefighters slide down a pole in the firehouse? Because it's too hard to slide up.

Why do oceans never go out of style?
They're always current.

Words to the wise:
Always go to other people's funerals. Otherwise, they won't go to yours.

Words to the wise:
If at first you don't succeed . . . then you'd better not go skydiving.

PRANK SQUAD

FAKE PET BARF: You can make some instant cat (or dog) vomit by softening chocolate chip cookies in milk. And if you want to gross out your friends, put your finger in the "barf," lick it and say "yum."

BANANA SNOT: For a joke that's snot nice, mash a slice of very ripe banana and place it in the middle of a tissue. Then pretend to blow your nose hard. Open the tissue in front of your friends—and have a taste. If you don't have a ripe banana, a cut-up peeled grape will also work.

MONSTROUS
AND GHOSTLY
GAGS

A monster is devouring an entire football team. Another monster comes along and argues that he's eating more than his share. "Okay," the first monster says. "I'll give you halfback."

How do ghosts get to school in the morning?
They take a ghoul bus.

Boy: "Daddy, when were you in Egypt?"
Father: "Egypt? I was never in Egypt."
Boy: "Then where did you get my mummy?"

A vampire bat came flapping in from the night covered in fresh blood and parked himself on the roof of the cave to get some sleep. Soon all the other bats smelled the blood and began asking him where he got it. He told them to knock it off and let him get some sleep, but they persisted until he gave in.

"Okay, follow me," he said and flew out of the cave with hundreds of bats behind him. Down through a valley they went, into a forest. Finally he slowed down, and the other bats excitedly milled around him.

"Do you see that tree over there?" he asked.

"Yes, yes, yes!" the bats all screamed in a frenzy.

"Good," said the first bat. "Because I didn't!"

How did Frankenstein know he was in love?
He felt that certain spark.

How do mummies hide?
They wear masking tape.

How do vampires get around on Halloween night?
By blood vessels.

How do you make a strawberry shake?
Sneak up behind it and yell "BOO!"

How does a monster count to 142?

On its fingers.

Little ghoul: "No fair! Why can you go to the Halloween party and I can't?"
Big ghoul: "Because I'm the mummy, that's why!"

What did the mommy ghost say to the baby ghost?

Don't spook until you're spooken to.

What do ghost babies wear on their feet?
Boo-tees.

What do ghosts serve for dessert?
Ice scream.

What do goblins and ghosts drink when they're hot and thirsty?
Ghoul-Aid.

What do skeletons say before they start to eat?
"Bone appétit!"

What do witches put in their hair?
Scare spray.

What do you call a giant monster who lives in the ocean and makes loud noises when he drinks?
A sea slurpant.

A robot mother and daughter walk by a hardware store, and the daughter stops to admire the paint cans displayed in the window. "I'm sorry," says the mother robot, "but your old coat will have to last you another year."

What do you call a haunted chicken?
A poultry-geist.

What do you call the ghost of a door-to-door salesperson?
A dead ringer.

What do you get when you cross a monster with a cat?
A mew-tation.

What do you get when you cross Bambi with a ghost?
Bamboo.

What does a ghost eat for lunch?
A boo-loney sandwich.

What giant monster lives in the mountains and hems men's suits?
The abominable sew-man.

What happens when a flying witch breaks the sound barrier?
You hear the broom boom.

What is a vampire's favourite holiday?
Fangsgiving.

What is Transylvania?
Dracula's terror-tory.

What kind of dog does Dracula have?
A bloodhound.

What kind of fur do you get from a werewolf?
As fur away as possible.

What kind of mistakes do ghosts make?
Boo boos.

What kind of monster is safe to put in the washing machine?
A wash-and-wear wolf.

What should you do when you find a ghost in your living room?
Offer him a sheet.

What should you do with overweight ghosts?
Exorcise them.

What would you find on a haunted beach?

A sand witch.

What would you get if you crossed a spaniel, a French poodle, a ghost and a rooster?

A cocker-poodle-boo.

What's a monster's favourite play?
Romeo and Ghouliet.

What's it like to be kissed by a vampire?
It's a pain in the neck.

What's pink and soft and found between a monster's teeth?
Slow runners.

When do ghosts usually appear?
Just before someone screams.

Where did the vampire open his savings account?
At the blood bank.

Where do baby ghosts go during the day?
To a dayscare centre.

Where do mummies go for a swim?
The Dead Sea.

Where do you store a werewolf?
In a were-house.

Where does Count Dracula wash his hair?
In the bat tub.

Where does Dracula water ski?
On Lake Eerie.

Who did Frankenstein take to the prom?
His ghoulfriend.

Why are most monsters covered in wrinkles?
Have you ever tried to iron a monster?

Why couldn't the young witch find a job?
She didn't have enough hex-perience.

Why did Count Dracula see his doctor?
He was always coffin.

Why did Godzilla visit Montreal on Saturday evening?
He wanted a night out on the town.

Why did the Blob stay home on Saturday night?
He was all dressed up with nowhere to goo.

Why did the ghoul cry when her pet zombie ran away?
Because he ran off with her mummy.

Why did the little skeleton feel left out?
He had no body to play with.

Why did the other kids have to let the vampire play baseball?
It was his bat.

Why did the vampire run screaming out of the restaurant?
He found out it was a stake house.

Why did the vampire's girlfriend dump him?
The relationship was too draining.

Why did the wizard drop out of school?
He couldn't spell.

Why didn't the two four-eyed monsters marry?
Because they could never see eye to eye to eye to eye.

Why do mummies make excellent spies?
They're good at keeping things under wraps.

Why do witches think they're funny?
Every time they look in the mirror, it cracks up.

Why don't abominable snowmen ever marry?
They always get cold feet.

Why don't monsters eat clowns?
They taste funny.

Why don't mummies take vacations?
They're afraid they'll relax and unwind.

Why don't skeletons go bungee jumping?
Because they don't have any guts.

Why should a skeleton drink lots of milk?
It's good for the bones.

Why wasn't the girl afraid of the monster?
It was a man-eating monster.

PRANK SQUAD

MUSICAL TORTURE: This one requires a musical birthday card. It will cost a little money, unless you have a musical card already. Remove the part that actually plays the music. Hide it near the victim (or in a pocket). The song, played over and over, is sure to drive anyone nuts.

CORN BARF: On a long ride in a car or on a bus or a train, you can really gross out the person next to you. All you need is a paper bag and a can of creamed corn (already opened). During the trip, tell your seatmate that you're feeling ill. Lurch forward, gag and pretend to vomit into the bag. After you've recovered, apologize to the victim, tell them you're feeling better and then help yourself.

CALLING ALL
ELEPHANTS

What do you call an elephant on a bike? Wheelie dangerous.

What do you call an elephant on the run?
An earthquake.

What do you call an elephant in a phone booth?
Stuck.

What do you call it when an elephant runs into two other elephants?
A three-squealer.

"Waiter!" yells a customer. "What's this elephant doing in my bowl of alphabet soup?"

The waiter comes over and says, "I suppose he's learning to read."

A man was walking by a restaurant when he saw a sign in the window that read, "We will pay $100 to anyone who orders something we can't make." The man went inside and sat down, and when the waitress came over, he asked for an elephant sandwich. She dug in her apron, pulled out a roll of bills and handed the man $100.

"What's the matter?" he asked. "No elephants today?"

"Oh, we have elephants, all right," she answered. "We're just all out of the big buns."

How can you tell if there's an elephant in your refrigerator?
There are footprints in the peanut butter.

How can you tell if there's an elephant in your bag of Oreos?
Read the list of ingredients.

How can you tell when there are two elephants in your refrigerator?
You can hear them giggling.

How can you tell when there are three elephants in your refrigerator?
Open the refrigerator door and check, silly.

How do you get an elephant to play the piano? You tickle her ivories.

How do you know if there's an elephant in front of you at the movies?
You can't see the screen.

How do you know there's an elephant in the bottom of your bunk bed?
Your nose touches the ceiling.

How do you make an elephant fly?
Well, first you take a great big zipper . . .

How do you make an elephant laugh?
Tickle him.

How do you stop an elephant from charging?
Take away his credit card.

How do you wake up a sleeping elephant?
Use an alarm clock.

How many elephants can you see on a clear night? It depends where you're standing.

Man: "I'll bet you $100 that I can lift an elephant with one hand."
Woman: "Ha! You're on!"
Man: "Fine! Go find me an elephant with one hand!"

What do you do if an elephant charges you?
Give him the money, quick!

What do you get when you cross a ghost with an elephant?
Wrinkled sheets.

What do you get when you cross an elephant with a kangaroo?
Big holes all over Australia.

What happened to the elephant that had a nervous breakdown?
They had to give him trunquilizers.

What should you do for an elephant with an upset stomach?
Stay as far away from her as possible.

What should you do when an elephant drives you up the wall?
Take away his licence.

What should you do with an elephant in a cast?
Make sure she knows her lines.

What steps would you take if you were being chased by an elephant?
Very big, quick ones.

What time is it when an elephant sits on a fence?
Time to get a new fence.

What's an elephant's favourite card game?
Memory.

What's large, blue and transparent on the outside?
An elephant stuck in a zip-lock bag.

What's large, grey and goes up and down?
An elephant in an exercise class.

What's large, grey and hard to spot?
A stain-resistant elephant.

What's large, grey and wears a trench coat?
An undercover elephant.

What's old, grey and wrinkled? A stale raisin pretending to be an elephant.

What's wide and pink?
An elephant's tutu.

What's the difference between an elephant and a cookie?
Have you ever tried dunking an elephant in milk?

What's the difference between an elephant and a loaf of bread?
If you don't know, then let's hope no one ever sends you to the corner store to buy a loaf of bread.

Where do elephants go to see art?
The peanut gallery.

Where do you find an elephant? Wherever you left her.

Why are elephants banned from public swimming pools?
They always drop their trunks.

Why are elephants known to hold grudges?
They can forgive, but they can't forget.

Why are elephants so wrinkly?
They're too big to fit on the ironing board.

Why did the elephant fall out of the tree?
Because it lost its balance.

So why did the second elephant fall out of the tree?
It was stuck to the first one.

Then why did the third elephant fall out of the tree?
It thought the other two were playing a game.

And why did the tree fall down? It wanted to be an elephant.

Why did the elephant forget?
She didn't renew her remembership.

Why did the elephant go running?
It wanted to jog its memory.

Why did the elephant leave the circus?
He was tired of working for peanuts.

Why did the elephant paint her toenails blue?
So she could hide in the blueberry bush.

Why did the elephant paint himself brown?
So he could hide in the box of raisins.

Why did the elephant paint himself red and white?

So he could hide in a can of Coca-Cola.

Why do elephants have big trunks?
So they have somewhere to put the groceries when they go shopping.

Why do elephants have trunks?
Because they don't have glove compartments.

Why do elephants wear sneakers?
So they can sneak up on peanuts.

Why don't elephants like computers?
They're afraid of the mouse.

Why don't elephants like elephant jokes?
They think they're Dumbo.

Why was the vacationing elephant so glum? The airline lost his trunk.

Knock, knock.
Who's there?
Gladys.
Gladys who?
Gladys you and not another elephant joke!

PRANK SQUAD

FAKE POO: Recruit a parent or other adult accomplice to help you with this recipe. You'll need the following ingredients: one cup (250 mL) of salt, one cup (250 mL) of all-purpose flour and one tablespoon (15 mL) of oil. Mix these ingredients together. Add water, a little at a time, until you have a large ball of dough. Using your hands, knead the dough on a board. The ball should be smooth and feel springy. If it's too dry, add a little more water. Now, mould a lump of the dough into the shape of dog poo. Place the poo on a baking dish. Bake it for an hour at 350°F (180°C) until it is hard. Let the poo cool, paint it brown, and wait for it to dry. Then decide where you're going to place it.

SMART ALECS AND SMART ALICES

"If you had a loonie and you asked your father for a toonie, how much money would you have?" the teacher asked the little boy.

"One dollar," replied the boy.

"You don't know your arithmetic," said the teacher.

"No," replied the boy. "You don't know my father."

"Jacob," said the teacher, "please make up a sentence using the word *lettuce*."

Jacob thought a minute and said, "Please lettuce leave class early today!"

"I didn't bring in my homework because I lost my memory," said Dan.

"When did this start?" his
teacher asked.

"When did what start?"

A child comes home from her
first day at school. Her father asks,
"Well, what did you learn today?"

The daughter replies, "Not
enough. They want me to come
back tomorrow."

A father and his small daughter were standing in front of the tiger's cage at the zoo. Dad was explaining how ferocious and strong tigers are, and the little girl was listening to him with a very serious expression.

"Daddy," she said finally, "if the tiger got out of his cage and ate you up . . ."

"Yes, dear?" asked the father.

"Which bus would I take home?"

A fisherman returned to shore with a giant marlin that was bigger and heavier than he was. On the way to the cleaning shed, he ran into a second fisherman, who had a string with a dozen baby minnows attached to it. The second fisherman looked at the marlin, turned to the first fisherman and said, "Only caught one, eh?"

A little girl came home early from school, so her father asked her why.

"Because I was the only one who could answer a question," she told him.

"What question was that?" said her father.

"Who threw the paper airplane at the teacher?"

A little girl was counting to ten for her math teacher.

"One, two, three, four, five," she said. "Six, seven, eight, ten!"

"Didn't you forget something?" prompted the teacher. "What happened to nine?"

"Well," replied the girl. "Seven eight nine."

A magician has been working on a cruise ship doing the same act for many years. The captain's parrot sits in the back row and watches him night after night. After a while, the parrot figures out how the tricks work and starts giving the secrets away to the audiences. The magician is annoyed but can't do anything, since the parrot belongs to the captain.

One day, the ship springs a leak and sinks. The magician manages to grab a plank of wood and floats on it. The parrot flies over and sits on the other end. They drift for three days without speaking. On the fourth day, the parrot looks at the magician and says, "Okay, I give up. Where did you hide the ship?"

A recent computer-science graduate starts his new job at a giant computer company. He's shocked when the manager tells him that his first job will be to sweep the floor. He protests, "But I can't do that, I'm a graduate of the Super-Duper-High-Tech Institute of Technology!"

The manager pauses and thinks for a second. "Well," she says, "then your first task will be to learn how to use a broom!"

Two women are out hiking when a bear starts chasing them. They climb a tree, but the bear climbs up the tree after them. The first woman gets her running shoes out of her backpack and puts them on. The second woman says, "What are you doing?"

The first woman says, "I figure when the bear gets close to us, we'll jump down and make a run for it."

The second woman says, "Are you crazy? You can't outrun a bear."

The first woman says, "I don't have to outrun the bear. I only have to outrun you!"

A teenager tells his father, "There's a problem with the car. It has water in the carburetor."

The father looks confused and says, "Water in the carburetor? That's ridiculous."

But the son insists. "I tell you, the car has water in the carburetor."

His father is starting to get a little nervous. "You don't even know what a carburetor is," he says. "I'll check it out. Where's the car?"

"In the pool."

A young man at a construction site always bragged that he was stronger than everyone else there. He especially made fun of the older workers. After a while, one of them had had enough. "Why don't you put your money where your mouth is?" he said. "I'll bet a week's pay that I can haul something in a wheelbarrow over to that building that you won't be able to wheel back."

"You're on," the bragger replied. "Let's see what you've got."

The old man reached out and grabbed the wheelbarrow by the handles. Then, nodding to the young man, he said with a smile, "All right. Get in."

A telemarketer calls a number on her list and gets a little boy on the line. He whispers, "Hello?"

The telemarketer asks, "Can I speak to your mommy?"

"No," the boy whispers. "She's busy."

The telemarketer says, "Okay, can I speak to your daddy, please?"

"He's busy too," the boy whispers.

Starting to get annoyed, the telemarketer says, "All right, is there another adult in the house?"

"Yes," the boy whispers again. "There's a policewoman."

"A policewoman?!" the salesperson gasps. "Can I speak to her?"

"No," whispers the boy. "She's busy too."

"Little boy," says the telemarketer, "with all of those adults in the house, *what* are they busy doing?"

After a short pause the little boy whispers, "Looking for me."

Amanda: "Our teacher talks to herself. Does yours?"
Justin: "Yes, but she doesn't realize it. She thinks we're listening."

Amy came to school without her homework assignment. "Where is your homework?" asked her teacher.

"I ate it," said Amy.

"But why did you do such a thing?" asked her teacher.

"You told the class yesterday that it would be a piece of cake."

David: "Close the window. It's cold outside."
Tom: "If I close the window, will it be warm outside?"

Chemistry teacher: "What is the formula for water?"
Student: "H-I-J-K-L-M-N-O."
Chemistry teacher: "Why would you give a silly answer like that?"
Student: "You said it was H to O!'

Customer: "Do you serve crabs here?"
Waiter: "We serve everyone. Sit right down."

Customer: "There's a fly in my soup."
Waiter: "That's possible. The chef used to be a tailor."

Customer: "This food isn't fit for a pig." Waiter: "I'll take it back then, and bring you some that is."

Customer: "How much are apples?"
Clerk: "Two dollars a pound."
Customer: "They're a dollar a pound across the street."
Clerk: "So buy them across the street."
Customer: "They're out of apples."
Clerk: "When I'm out of apples, mine are also a dollar a pound."

Customer: "How much are the chocolates?"
Clerk: "Two for a quarter."
Customer: "How much is one?"
Clerk: "Fifteen cents."
Customer: "Okay, I'll have the other one."

Customer: "Waiter, my vegetables just punched me!"
Waiter: "That's because they're black-eyed peas."

Customer: "Waiter, there's a fly in my alphabet soup!"
Waiter: "That's no fly, that's a spelling bee."

Customer: "Waiter, there's a fly in my soup!"
Waiter: "Don't worry, sir, we won't charge you extra for it."

Customer: "Waiter, there's a fly in my soup!"
Waiter: "Shhh. You're making the other customers jealous."

Customer: "Waiter, there's a jack in my soup!"
Waiter: "That's because we made it with bean stock."

Customer: "What is this insect in my soup?"
Waiter: "I wish you wouldn't ask me. I don't know one bug from another."

Customer: "Yesterday there wasn't a fly in my soup, but tonight there is one!"
Waiter: "That's because we're a fly-by-night operation, sir."

Customer: "Waiter, there's a fly doing the breaststroke in my soup!"
Waiter: "You're mistaken, sir. That's the butterfly."

Customer: "What's this fly doing in my soup?"

Waiter: "The backstroke?"

Customer: "Waiter, what's this fly doing in my soup?"
Waiter: "Looks like he's drowning, ma'am."

Customer: "Why are there antlers on my filet mignon?"
Waiter: "Sorry, sir, that must be a moose steak."

Customer: "Why is my doughnut all smashed?"
Waitress: "You said you wanted a coffee and doughnut—and to step on it."

What did the weather announcer say about his meteorology test?

"It was a breeze with only a few foggy patches."

Danny: "Miss Ratkin, we ain't got no chalk."

Miss Ratkin: "Danny, you mean, 'I don't have any chalk. You don't have any chalk. They don't have any chalk.' Do you understand what I'm trying to say?"

Danny: "Yes. So what happened to all the chalk?"

Emily: "Teacher, will you pass the nuts?"

Teacher: "No, I think I'll flunk them."

James was really excited when he came home from school. His mother asked him for the good news, and he said, "I got a hundred in school today! In two subjects!"

James's mother was overjoyed. She said, "My goodness, how did you do that?"

James said, "I got a fifty in math and a fifty in science."

Joe and Moe sat down in a restaurant, took out their lunch boxes and began eating their sandwiches.

"You can't eat your own sandwiches here," the waitress told them.

So they swapped sandwiches.

Justin: "The dog ate my homework."

Teacher: "Justin, you don't have a dog."

Justin: "It was a stray."

Marcia asked Bill, "Was that the clock tocking earlier?"

"Not to me," said Bill. "It wouldn't even give me the time of day."

Mother: "Are you doing your homework right now?"

Son: "I'm doing my homework. Whether it's right is another matter."

On the first day of class, the teacher asked any troublemakers to stand up. After a few moments of silence, a shy little girl stood up. "Are you a troublemaker?" the teacher asked.

"No," replied the girl. "I just hate to see you standing there all by yourself."

On the first day of school, the kindergarten teacher said to her class, "If anyone has to go to the washroom, please hold up two fingers."

A little voice from the back row asked, "How will that help?"

One by one, a class of grade five students were called on to make sentences with words chosen by their teacher. Nick didn't often participate in class, so his teacher was glad when she saw him raise his hand to give it a try.

"Nick," said the teacher, "make a sentence with the words *defeat, defence, deduct* and *detail*."

Nick thought for a few minutes and smiled. He shouted, "Defeat of deduct went over defence before detail!"

Passenger: "Does this train stop in Halifax?"
Conductor: "If it doesn't, you're going to hear a terrible splash."

Peter: "How do you like going to school?"

Rita: "I like it. And I also like coming home. It's the in-between part that I'm not crazy about.

Principal: "Scott, did you really call your teacher a meanie?"

Scott: "Yes, I did."

Principal: "And is it true you called her a wicked old witch?"

Scott: "Yes, it is."

Principal: "And did you also call her a tomato-nosed beanbag?"

Scott: "No, but I'll remember that for next time!"

Sally's parents were going out, and Sally said, "For 20 bucks, Dad, I'll be good."

"Oh, please," said her father. "When I was your age, I was good for nothing."

Sam: "Would you punish me for something I didn't do?"
Teacher: "No, of course not."
Sam: "Good, because I didn't do my homework."

**Michael: "So what's the worst thing at the school cafeteria?"
Emily: "The food."**

**Student: "I don't think I deserve a zero on this test."
Teacher: "Neither do I, but that's the lowest grade I can give you."**

Teacher: "If you add 250 plus 6, divide by 4, and multiply by 14, what do you get?"
Suzie: "The wrong answer."

Teacher: "Amy, I've had to send you to the principal's office every day this week. What do you have to say for yourself?"
Amy: "I'm glad it's Friday!"

Teacher: "Brad, how do you spell Saskatchewan?"
Brad: "S-a-s-c-a-t-c-h-e-w-a-n-n."
Teacher: "No, that's wrong."
Brad: "Maybe it's wrong, but you asked me how I spell it."

Teacher: "Class, someone has stolen my wallet out of my desk. It had $100 in it. I know you're all basically good kids, so I'm willing to offer a reward of $10 to whoever returns it."
Voice at the back of the room: "I'm offering $20!"

Teacher: "I'm giving a quiz today, but first I'll take attendance. Tom?"

Tom: "Present."

Teacher: "Sandra?"

Sandra: "Present."

Teacher: "Kim?"

Kim: "Present."

Teacher: "Simon?"

Simon: "Pass."

Teacher: "We'll see about that."

Teacher: "James, do you use bad words?"
James: "No, sir."
Teacher: "Do you disobey your parents?"
James: "No, sir."
Teacher: "Come now, you must do something wrong every once in a while!"
James: "I tell lies."

Teacher: "Maggie, why do you always get so dirty?"
Maggie: "Because I'm a lot closer to the ground than you are."

Teacher: "Mr. Jones, I asked you to come in to discuss your son's appearance."

Mr. Jones: "Why? What's wrong with his appearance?"

Teacher: "He hasn't made one in this classroom since September."

Teacher: "Sam, if I put 12 marbles in my right pocket, 15 marbles in my left pocket and 31 marbles in my back pocket, what would I have?"

Sam: "Heavy pants!"

Teacher: "What is a synonym?"

Mary: "It's a word you use when you don't know how to spell the other one."

Teacher: "What's the definition of illegal?" Mary: "A sick bird."

Boy: "Isn't our principal stupid?"
Girl: "Hey, do you know who I am?"
Boy: "No, why should I?"
Girl: "I'm the principal's daughter."
Boy: "Do you know who I am?"
Girl: "No."
Boy: "Thank goodness!"

It's not the school that bothers me.
It's the principal of the thing.

Teacher: "Who wrote *Anne of Green Gables*?"

Student: "Gee, I didn't know they had post offices then. But I'd guess it was one of her close friends."

The class was studying for a history test when one student said, "I wish we lived way back in time."

"Why is that?" asked the teacher.

"Then there would be less history to learn!"

The conductor of a symphony orchestra was having a lot of trouble with one of the percussionists. The conductor talked and talked and talked with her, but her performance didn't improve. Finally, in front of the whole orchestra, the conductor said, "When a musician can't play her instrument well and doesn't get better when she is given help, they take away the instrument, give her two sticks, and make her a drummer."

A voice from the percussion section said, "And if she can't play even that, they take away one of her sticks and make her a conductor."

Three old men have just arrived in heaven and are attending an orientation meeting. They are asked, "When you are at the funeral and your friends and families are mourning, what would you like to hear them say about you?"

The first guy says, "I'd like to hear them say that I was a great doctor and a great family man."

The second guy says, "I would like them to say that I was a wonderful husband and schoolteacher, and that I made a huge difference in our children of tomorrow."

The last guy thinks a moment and says, "I think I'd like to hear them say, 'Look! He's moving!'"

A man drove his car into a ditch in a remote area in the country. Luckily, a local farmer came to help with her big, strong horse named Buddy. She hitched Buddy up to the car and yelled, "Pull, Nellie, pull!" Buddy didn't move. Then the farmer hollered, "Pull, Buster, pull!" Buddy didn't budge. Once more the farmer commanded, "Pull, Coco, pull!" Nothing. Then the farmer casually said, "Pull, Buddy, pull!" and the horse easily dragged the car out of the ditch. The motorist was most grateful and very curious. He asked the farmer why she had called her horse by the wrong name three times. The farmer said, "Oh, Buddy is blind, and if he thought he was the only one pulling, he wouldn't even try!"

PRANK
SQUAD

FAKE POO #2: Soak an empty toilet tissue roll in warm water. Tear the soaked paper into small pieces and squeeze them together in your hand, moulding the cardboard until it looks like a piece of poo. Add more water if needed to hold the pieces together. Leave the poo in just the right place—next to your friend's computer, for example, or on your sister's desk.

HAPPY BIRTHDAY: This *nice* joke is based on the old Kick Me sign that you tape to someone's back. On a friend's birthday, tape a sign on his back that says, It's My Birthday. He'll be shocked by how many people wish him a happy birthday.

THIS STUFF
IS FOR REAL

FUNNY HEADLINES

Man Takes First Prize in Dog Show

Grandmother of Eight Makes Hole in One

Safety Expert Says School Bus Passengers Should Be Belted

Astronaut Takes Blame for Gas in Spacecraft

Stolen Paintings Found by Tree

Miners Refuse to Work after Death

ADS IN NEWSPAPERS

Dog for sale. Eats anything.
Is very fond of children.

Dinner Special. Roast Beef, $4.50.
Chicken or Turkey, $4.00.
Children, $3.00.

Lost—scarf by a small boy
with red and white stripes.

For sale. Antique desk, suitable
for lady with thick legs and
large drawers.

Lost. Brown-and-white mutt.
Has three legs, is blind and is
missing one ear and part of its tail.
Answers to the name "Lucky."

SIGNS OF THE TIMES

Barbershop:
Haircuts while you wait.

Dry cleaner:
Drop your pants here.

Health food store:
Closed due to illness.

Towing company:
We don't charge an arm and a leg.
We want tows.

Travel agency:
Please go away.

Butcher shop:
We will meat all your needs.

Computer store:
Out for a quick byte.

Dry cleaner: We do not tear your clothing with machinery. We do it carefully by hand.

Used car dealer: Why go elsewhere to be cheated? Come here first!

Outside a hotel:
We need inn-experienced people.

Laundromat: Please remove your clothes when the dryer has stopped.

At a washroom in an office building: Toilet out of order. Please use floor below.

PRANK
SQUAD

CARAMEL ONIONS: This prank works
at Halloween or any other time in
the fall. Find a few apple-sized
onions, and instead of making caramel or candy apples, use a surprise
ingredient—onions! It's easiest if
you follow the recipe on the bag of
caramels or use the ingredients of a
candy apple kit. Peel off the skin,
but also a few layers of the onion
before you begin dipping it in the
heated caramel or candy mixture.
Make sure no part of the onion is
showing when you insert the stick.
You may want to give several friends
the real thing—a caramel or candy
apple—and just one or two victims
the onion version.

WHAT DO YOU GET? AND WHAT'S THE DIFFERENCE?

What do you get from
a pampered cow?
Spoiled milk.

What do you
get if you cross
a bear with a
skunk?
Winnie the
Pee-yew!

What do you get if
you cross a duck with
an alligator?
A quack-odile.

What do you get if you cross a Jedi knight with a toad?
Star Warts.

What do you get if you cross a mouth with a tornado?
A tongue twister.

What do you get when you cross a baby goat with a porcupine?
One stuck-up kid!

What do you get when you cross a bed with a kitchen appliance?
A four-poster toaster.

What do you get when you cross a cat with a vacuum cleaner?
I don't know, but it sure drinks a lot of milk!

What do you get when you cross a centipede with a parrot?
A walkie-talkie.

What do you get when you cross a chicken with a centipede?
Drumsticks for everyone.

What do you get when you cross a comedian with crochet?
A knit wit.

What do you get when you cross a computer with a toad?
A wart processor.

What do you get when you cross a dog with a soldier?
A pooper trooper.

What do you get when you cross a dog with an omelette?
Pooched eggs.

What do you get when you cross a golf club with a car?
A backseat driver.

What do you get when you cross a lion with a parrot?
I don't know, but when it talks, you'd better listen!

What do you get when you cross a sheep with a kung fu master?
Lamb chops.

What do you get when you cross a sink with a bugle?
Taps.

What do you get when you cross a thousand screech owls with a thousand roosters?
A big headache first thing in the morning.

What do you get when you cross an ear of corn with a spider?
Cob webs.

What do you get when you cross an orchestra with a bunch of monkeys?
A chimp-phony.

What do you get when you cross chocolate powder with a magic dragon?
Cocoa Puffs.

What do you get when you cross Cinderella with a barber?
Glass clippers.

What do you get when you cross Mickey's girlfriend with a shrinking machine?
Mini Mouse.

What do you get when you cross your brother with an owl?
A wise guy.

What do you get when you drop a piano on an army base?
A major B-flat.

What do you get when you grill a Barbie doll?
A Barbiecue.

What do you get when you cross a fish with an elephant?
Swimming trunks.

What do you get when you put a kitten in a photo-copier?
A copycat.

What's the difference between a dog who sticks his head out the car window and your little brother or sister?
One's a neck in the pane, the other's a pain in the neck.

What's the difference between a red light and a green light?
The colour.

What's the difference between a skateboard and an elephant?
One has four wheels, the other doesn't.

What's the difference between a summer dress in winter and a pulled molar? *One is too thin, the other tooth out.*

What's the difference between a *Tyrannosaurus rex* and an elephant? One dismembers, the other remembers.

What's the difference between an old loonie and a new dime?
90 cents.

What's the difference between an onion and a banjo?
I wouldn't cry if you chopped up the banjo.

What's the difference between Neptune and Earth?
There's a world of difference.

What's the difference between teachers and trains? Trains say, "Choo Choo!" and teachers say, "Spit that gum out!"

PRANK SQUAD

LABEL CRAZE: Put yellow sticky notes on all the cans and packages in a kitchen cupboard. Use either the real names of the items or silly names. This is sure to drive someone nuts for weeks (at least).

BATHROOM HUMOUR: Unroll the toilet paper partway and tape a raisin on the last sheet of paper you've unrolled. Then roll the roll back up and wait for your unsuspecting victim to start unrolling. (A fake bug should do the job too.) Unscrew the lid of a shampoo container, cover the opening with plastic wrap (you may need to use an elastic band), and screw the lid back on. When the person showering squeezes the container, nothing will come out.

LAW
AND
DISORDER

A police officer saw a woman sitting in her car with a tiger next to her. The officer said, "It's against the law to have that tiger here on the street! Take him to the zoo."

The next day the police officer saw the same woman in the same car with the same tiger. He said, "I thought I told you to take that tiger to the zoo!"

The woman replied, "I did. He liked it so much, today we're going to the beach!"

A writer was convicted of a terrible, bloody murder. After 10 years in solitary confinement, she was brought before a judge to see whether she felt remorse. "Do you feel sorry for what you did?" asked the judge.

"Well, I . . ." replied the writer. After a moment, the writer was marched back to prison.

After 20 more years, the writer was a new woman. She argued that she had given up her criminal ways for good and applied for parole. "I can't let you go free," said the judge.

"Why not?" asked the writer.

"Well," said the judge, "you never finished your sentence."

Defendant: "Your Honour, I'm not guilty of robbery. I'm a locksmith."

Judge: "Well, what were you doing at the scene of the crime when the police arrived?"

Defendant: "Just making a bolt for the door!"

Judge: "You look familiar. Have we met before?"

Defendant: "Yes—I taught your daughter to play the drums, remember?"

Judge: "Life in prison for you!"

Did Sheriff Pat Garrett shoot Billy the Kid in the end?

No, he shot him right through the heart.

Did you hear about the crook at the scale factory?
Yeah, he got a weigh.

How come the police didn't catch the woman who robbed the dry cleaner?
She made a clean getaway.

How did the mutt defend his crime?
He blamed it on bad breeding.

How did the police know the blacksmith's signature was a fake?
It was forged.

How did the police know the photographer was guilty?
They found his prints all over the scene of the crime.

How did the robber get caught at the art gallery?
He was framed.

How did the runaway barber escape from the police?
He knew all the short cuts.

How did they catch the crooks at the pig farm?
Someone squealed.

How was the fish farm robbed?
By hook and by crook.

Judge: "I find you guilty and I'm giving you a choice: $15,000 or six months in jail."
Defendant: "Your Honour, I'll take the money!"

Judge: "Order in the court!"
Defendant: "I'll have a
cheeseburger and fries,
Your Honour."

Police officer (putting handcuffs
on a crook): "If I were you, I'd get
myself a good lawyer."
Crook: "Officer, if I could afford a
good lawyer, I wouldn't have tried
to rob that bank."

Policeman: "Why did you hit
that tree?"
Driver: "Don't blame me! I honked
at it, but it wouldn't move."

A traffic cop pulls over a driver who has been speeding and asks him, "Didn't you see the speed limit signs posted on this road?"

"Why, officer," said the driver, "I was going much too fast to read those tiny little signs."

Traffic officer: "Did you know this is a one-way street?"

Driver: "Of course—I'm only driving one way!"

What did the cops tell the mime when they arrested her?
"You still have the right to remain silent."

What did the Northwest Territories judge ask the defendant? "Where were you on the night of October to April?"

What did the police do with the hamburger? *They grilled him.*

Why didn't the police arrest the runner?
She had a good track record.

What did the police officer say when he caught the woman who had stolen the office equipment?
"Just give me the fax, ma'am."

What did the zero say when asked if he had committed the crime?
"I did nothing!"

What do you call a court case about swimwear?
A bathing suit.

What do you call it when crooks go surfing?
A crime wave.

What do you call it when someone crashes into a police officer?
A run-in with the law.

What do you get when you cross a bank robber with the Invisible Man?
You get away with it.

What do you get when you cross a judge with poison ivy?
Rash decisions.

What do you get when you cross a police officer with an alarm clock?
A crime watch.

What happened to the robber who stole the lamp?
Oh, he got a very light sentence.

Why couldn't the cops catch the wallpaper thief?
There was a big cover-up.

Why couldn't the thunderclouds pull off the bank heist?
When the alarm went off, they all bolted.

Why did the cops arrest the baseball player?
They heard he had stolen third base.

Why did the cops hang out at the coffee shop?
In case someone got mugged.

Why did the cops plant cat-nip at the scene of the crime?
To catch a cat burglar.

Why did the cops show up at the amusement park?
They heard somebody was being taken for a ride.

Why did the cucumber need a lawyer?
It was in a pickle.

Why did the police investigate the seafood restaurant?
They knew something fishy was going on.

Why did the police officers arrest the python after the accident?
It was a hiss and run.

Why did the police raid the comic book store?
They were doing a strip search.

Why did the sticker need a lawyer?
It was ripped off.

Why did the strawberry need a lawyer?
It was in a jam.

Why didn't the police search for the missing rutabaga?
They knew it would turnip somewhere soon.

Why was the artist arrested for graffiti?
He had to draw the line somewhere.

Why was the comedian accused of assaulting her audience?
She gagged them and left them in stitches.

Why was the mime unhelpful in reporting the incident?
She couldn't say what had happened.

PRANK SQUAD

SPAGHETTI SNEEZE: Help yourself to a small handful of plain cooked pasta. Hide it in your hand and pretend to sneeze just as you throw the gooey mass over your face or into someone's lap.

BED BUGS: Put some bugs in your victim's bed. But don't use the real thing. A small piece of fake fur under the covers will work just as well. An old banana skin does the job too.

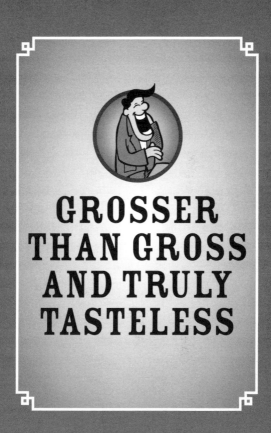

GROSSER THAN GROSS AND TRULY TASTELESS

Did you hear about the giant with diarrhea?
It's all over town now.

Chuck goes to his doctor and says, "Doctor, I'm a little embarrassed to talk about this, but I seem to be barfing a lot."

The doctor says, "Well, I'm glad you feel you can bring this up, Chuck."

What do Camembert cheese and a nose have in common?
They can both smell and be runny.

Why was the car smelly?
It had too much gas.

Did you hear about the woman who bought a musical toilet seat?

Poor thing! Every time she tries to sit down, it plays "O Canada!"

One day a woman walked into the doctor's office. She said, "Doctor, I have a problem. I fart all the time. They don't smell, and they're silent. They don't even bother me! In fact, I have farted 20 times since I entered the room, and you didn't even know! Do you have a diagnosis?"

The doctor gave the woman some pills and sent her on her way.

The woman came back to the doctor's office a week later and said, "Doctor! What were those pills you gave me? Now, when I fart, they stink!"

The doctor replied, "Great, now that we've got your sinuses cleared up, let's work on your hearing."

A very pretty woman is sitting in an expensive restaurant one evening. She is waiting for her date and wants to be sure everything is perfect. She decides to check how her hair looks. As she bends over in her chair to get a mirror from her purse, she accidentally farts quite loudly just as the waiter walks up. She sits up, horribly embarrassed and red in the face, sure that everyone in the restaurant has heard the fart. She decides to blame it on the waiter, and she turns to him and orders, "Stop that!"

The waiter looks at her calmly and replies, "Sure, lady. Where was it headed?"

Two dragons are chasing a knight in armour. Just as they are about to catch him, the first dragon says, "You remembered to bring the barbecue sauce this time, right?"

The second dragon answers, "Yes. And I hope you remembered the can opener."

Visitor: "Is your baby spoiled?"
Mother: "I don't think so. I just need to change her diaper."

What should you do to keep a corpse from smelling?

Nothing—dead people can't smell!

What's the difference between a booger and broccoli? Kids don't eat broccoli.

What were the little snots afraid of when they went to bed?
The booger man.

What's brown and sounds like a bell?
Dung.

What's invisible and smells like carrots?
Bunny farts.

If it takes a cup of chocolate chips to make a batch of chocolate chip cookies and a cup of peanut butter to make a batch of peanut butter cookies, then does it take a cup of Girl Guides to make a batch of Girl Guide cookies?

Why did Tigger stick his head in the toilet?
He was looking for Pooh.

Tasteless Song—To the Tune of "When the Saints Go Marching In"

Oh when the ants
Get in our food,
It puts us in an awful mood.
We find legs in our egg salad,
When the ants get in our food.

Oh when the dog
Drools on our meal,
To eat at all loses its appeal.
We find slobber on our sandwich,
When the dog drools on our meal.

Oh when the sand
Gets in our lunch,
Potato chips have extra crunch.
We find grit in ground-beef patties,
When the sand gets in our lunch.

Oh when the flies
Land on our spread,
We've no desire to be fed.
We find bugs on our bologna,
When the flies land on our spread.

Next time we dine
We'll stay inside.
Our hungry mouths we'll open wide.
Within walls, it's safe to swallow,
Next time we'll dine inside.

PRANK SQUAD

MORE TOILET FUN: Unroll several sheets of toilet paper. Write messages on the last few sheets you unroll. (Smile! or Hello! or Yuck!) Then neatly roll the sheets back into place.

FAKE BLOOD: There are quite a few recipes for fake blood. Here's one that gives just the right colour and stickiness. You'll need a small jar with a lid that screws on tightly, a teaspoon, a tablespoon, an eyedropper, red food colouring, water, corn starch and corn syrup. Here's what to do: In the jar, mix three or four drops of food colouring, two teaspoons (10 mL)of water, and one or two teaspoons (5 or 10 mL) of cornstarch. Cover the jar and shake it well.

CROSSING
THE ROAD

Why did the chicken cross the playground?
To get to the other slide.

Why did the cow cross the road?
To get to the udder side.

Why did the daredevil cross the road?
She wanted to play chicken.

Why did the dog cross the road twice?
She was trying to fetch a boomerang.

Why did the muddy chicken cross the road and then cross back?
He was a dirty double-crosser.

Why did the rooster cross the road?
He wanted something to crow about.

Why did the rooster cross the road?
To show he wasn't a chicken.

Why did the chicken bounce across the road?
She was a rubber chicken.

Why did the rubber chicken cross the road?
She wanted to stretch her legs.

Why didn't the hen cross the road?
Because she was too chicken.

Why did the lollipop cross the road?
Because it was stuck on the chicken.

Why did the chicken cross the road?
She thought it would be eggciting.

Why did the chicken cross the road?
To get the National Post. *Get it?*
No.
Me neither. I get the Globe and Mail.

Why did the atom cross the road?
Because it was time to split.

What do you call it when a chicken stumbles as it crosses the street?
A road trip.

Why couldn't the bodybuilder cross the road?
The traffic was too heavy.

Why did the turtle cross the road?
To get to the Shell station.

Why didn't the skeleton cross the road? Because he didn't have the guts.

Why did the booger cross the road?
Because it was being picked on.

PRANK SQUAD

EATING DUDU: Want to really gross out your classmates? Tell them you've eaten dudu. After they recover from the shock, tell them it's an African specialty made of fried, salted bugs: ants, bees, crickets and cicadas. Yum!

MONSTER CHILD: Scare the living daylights out of your little brother! Find a picture of the creepiest, scariest, grossest monster you can and hide it somewhere in your house. Lead your younger sibling to the hiding place, swear him to secrecy, then reveal the photo and say it's a photo of him when he was born.

WHY—AND HOW—DID THEY DO IT?

Why did Bobby tie a clock to his palms?
He wanted to have time on his hands.

Why did Captain Kirk sneak into the ladies' room?
He wanted to go where no man had gone before.

Why did everyone find the baker funny?
He had a rye sense of humour.

Why did the 25-watt bulb flunk out of school?
He wasn't very bright.

Why did the baker sell his bread only to the rich and famous?
He wanted to work for the upper crust.

Why did the band eat rabbit stew for a whole week?
They wanted to play hip-hop.

Why did the Beatles break up?
They started to bug each other.

Why did the bird fall out of the tree?
It was dead.

Why did the bird make fun of everyone?
It was a mockingbird.

Why did the bird sit on the fish?
The fish was a perch.

Why did the boy eat the lamp?
His mother told him to have a light snack.

Why did the boy font break up with the girl font?
She wasn't his type.

Why did the boy give his teacher a PC?
The store was out of Apples.

Why did the boy quit his job at the eraser factory?
His work rubbed him the wrong way.

Why did the boy stop practising the violin at Christmas? Because his mother asked for peace on Earth.

Why did the bug family stay home on their last vacation?
The roach motel was full.

Why did the cabinet go to the psychiatrist?
It kept talking to its shelf.

Why did the chimp sell his banana store?
He was tired of all the monkey business.

Why did the clock need a holiday?
It was all wound up.

Why did the coffee shop waitress love her job?
Because there were so many perks.

Why did the comedian put on his sneakers?
He wanted to tell a running joke.

Why did the computer geek take up photography?
He wanted his own dorkroom.

Why did the doughnut make a dentist's appointment?
Because it needed a filling!

Why did the drummer bring a chicken to band practice? He needed new drumsticks.

Why did the Earthling fall in love with the alien?
Because she was out of this world.

Why did the egg accuse the chef of cruelty?
He put her in a bowl and beat her.

Why did the engineer leave locomotive school?
She felt she already had enough training.

Why did the fight fans keep getting punched?
Because they were sitting in the box seats.

Why did the fisherman go deaf?
He had problems with his herring.

Why did the geek turn on his computer on a hot day?
He wanted to open the Windows.

Why did the human cannonball choose this line of work?
He wanted to be a big shot.

Why did the insect collector toss the butter dish across the restaurant?
He wanted to see the butter fly.

Why did the janitor quit his job?
He wanted to make a clean sweep.

Why did the journalist go to the ice cream parlour?
She wanted to get the scoop.

Why did the kid throw quarters under the car wheel?
He wanted to help change a tire.

Why did the mama bread get mad at her kids?
They were always loafing around.

Why did the mama ladybug ground her kids?
They were bugging her.

Why did the man take his
computer to a clinic?
It had a virus.

Why did the mandolin
go the psychiatrist?
*It was tired of being
high-strung.*

Why did the microprocessor
always write form letters?
It was an impersonal computer.

Why did the mother
always put on a helmet
before she used the
computer?
*Because she was afraid it
would crash!*

453

Why did the other vegetables like the corn?
She was always willing to lend an ear.

Why did the pregnant woman race to the hospital?
She wanted to have a speedy delivery.

Why did the restaurant on the moon go out of business?
It lacked atmosphere.

Why did the Rice Krispies go snap, quackle, pop?
Crackle ducked out.

Why did the salad make the chef turn around?
She didn't want him to see her dressing.

Why did the sheet music run away from the singer?
She kept hitting all the notes.

Why did the silly astronaut turn off all the lights on the spaceship? *He wanted to travel at the speed of dark.*

Why did the stagehand quit her job?
She wanted a change of scenery.

Why did the stoplight turn red?
*Wouldn't you if you had to change
in the middle of the street?*

**Why did the student put on eye-
liner and mascara at school?**
*Because the teacher said she was
giving the class a makeup exam.*

**Why did the student take her
math homework to gym class?**
*She wanted to work out her
problems.*

Why did the student think his teacher was colour-blind?
Because every time she caught him cheating, she said she was seeing red.

Why did the teacher put elastic bands on her students' heads?
So they could make snap decisions.

Why did the teacher wear sunglasses?
Because the students were so bright.

Why did the teapot blush?
He thought the kettle was whistling at him.

Why did Tim Hortons stop making doughnuts?
They were tired of the hole business.

Why did the tire need a holiday?
It couldn't take the pressure any longer.

Why did the trombone player get kicked out of the band?
Because he kept letting things slide.

Why did the upholsterer quit her job?
She was worn out.

Why did the watch go on vacation?
To unwind.

Why did the woman attach her computer to a fishing rod?
Someone told her to hook it up.

Why did the woman divorce the grape?
She was tired of raisin kids.

Why did the young woman take the job at the glue factory?
It was fast paste.

Why didn't the cashier get the punchline?
It didn't register.

Why didn't the man fix dinner?
Because people always say, "If it ain't broke, don't fix it!"

Why didn't the opera singer get a job on the cruise ship?

Because she was afraid of the high Cs.

Why didn't the shrimp share his dessert?
He was shellfish.

Why didn't they let the wildcat into school?
They knew he was a cheetah.

How did Mary, Mary, Quite Contrary, make her garden grow?
With water.

How did the astronaut feel when he ran into the alien with six lasers for arms?
Stunned.

How did the baker get so wealthy?
He made a lot of dough.

How did the captain know when his ship was going down?
He had a sinking feeling.

How did the desk calendar snub the calculator?
She wouldn't give him a date.

How did the ghost fix the hole in his sheet?
With a pumpkin patch.

How did the praying mantis get the gossip on the grasshopper?
The grasshopper's phone was bugged.

How did the trampolinist beat the prize-fighter?
Every time she was knocked down, she bounced right back.

PRANK SQUAD

BEDTIME SCAMS:

1. Wear plastic fangs, and convince your parents that you're a vampire.

2. Explain that the country has recently gone on Daylight Super-Saving Time, so it's actually only four o'clock in the afternoon.

3. Tell your parents that your science homework was to stay up and look for shooting stars and that you'll flunk if you don't see at least one.

4. Insist that you must stand guard all night in order to finally get that monster in your closet.

5. Laugh and say, "I'm already in bed! You're just dreaming that I'm still awake!"

6. Explain that you are practising for New Year's Eve and have to stay up all night long.

NOT THE
BRIGHTEST
CRAYON IN
THE BOX

A man phoned an airline office in Toronto.

"How long does it take to fly to Halifax?" he asked.

"Just a minute," the clerk told him.

"Thanks," the man said before hanging up.

A repair technician got a call from a computer user. The user told her that his computer was not working. He described the problems he was having, and the technician told him that his computer needed to be serviced. She told him, "Unplug the power cord and bring it here to get fixed." Later on, the man showed up at the repair shop with the power cord in his hand.

A woman frantically calls the fire department to report a fire in her neighbourhood.

The dispatcher asks, "How do we get there?"

The woman replies, "Don't you still have those big red fire trucks?"

A woman is sitting in a park one day, watching two men work. The first man digs a hole, then the second man fills it back up with dirt. Then the first man digs another hole, and again, the second man fills it back up. They keep doing this over and over again. Finally, the woman asks them, "Why do you keep digging holes and then filling them back in?"

One of the guys replies, "Well, usually there's a third guy here who puts in the tree, but he's off sick today."

A woman walks over to a guard at the museum. "How old do you think these dinosaur bones are?" she asks.

"Oh," he replies. "They're three million and three years and two months old."

"That's amazing," the woman says. "How can you be so exact?"

"Well," the guard answers. "They were three million years old when I started working here, and that was three years and two months ago."

A young woman is speeding down a highway when she is stopped by a police officer. The officer asks if he could please see her driver's licence. The woman replies angrily, "I wish you guys would make up your minds. Just yesterday you take away my licence, and now you expect me to show it to you!"

A sailor met a pirate, and they started to talk about their adventures. The pirate had a peg leg, a hook and an eye patch. The sailor asked, "So, how did you end up with the peg leg?"

The pirate replied, "We were in a storm, and I was swept overboard. A shark bit my leg off."

"Wow!" exclaimed the sailor. "How did you get that hook?"

"Well," replied the pirate, "we boarded an enemy ship and were battling other sailors with swords. One of them cut off my hand."

"Incredible!" remarked the sailor. "How did you get the eye patch?"

"A seagull dropping fell into my eye," replied the pirate.

"You lost your eye to a seagull dropping?"

"Well," said the pirate, "it was my first day with the hook."

An astronaut graduated near the bottom of his class. On his first mission into space, he was teamed up with a monkey. They each got an envelope that they were to open once they got into orbit, with instructions for their mission. Once they had blasted off and were in space, the monkey opened his envelope, read the instructions, and began flicking buttons and hitting switches. The astronaut opened up his envelope and found a note that read, "Feed the monkey."

Annie: "I thought you were going bear hunting!"
Danny: "I was. But I only made it as far as the highway."
Annie: "What happened?"
Danny: "Well, I saw a road sign that said "Bear left," so I came home!"

Customer: "I cleaned my computer and now it's broken!"

Repair technician: "What did you clean it with?"

Customer: "Water and soap."

Repair technician: "You're not supposed to use water to clean a computer!"

Customer: "I don't think it was the water that broke it . . . I think it was the spin cycle."

George: "What a fabulous singer Céline Dion is."
Michelle: "Well, if I had her voice, I'd be just as good."

How do you make a stupid person laugh on Boxing Day?
Tell him a joke on Christmas Eve.

I'm really glad I don't like broccoli. If I did, I'd eat it. And I can't stand the taste of it.

Jane (on the phone): "I'm afraid my daughter can't go to school today."
Principal: "Oh, that's too bad. And to whom am I talking?"
Jane: "This is my mother speaking."

Once upon a time there was a rich, dumb king who had a beautiful daughter. One day, a fierce dragon came and carried the daughter off into his cave high on a mountaintop.

"Just wait a minute, mister," said the daughter. "Dragons aren't real. Here, I'll show you." And she pulled a pocket encyclopedia out of her purse.

The dragon put on his reading glasses. "Hmm . . . aardvarks, beavers . . . gazelles . . . unicorns, vultures . . . zebras, zebus, zombies. Nope, no dragons." And the dragon instantly disappeared.

"How did you escape from that horrible dragon?" the king asked his daughter.

"Easy. I proved to him that dragons don't exist. Now are you or aren't you going to buy me that pet unicorn for my birthday?"

Randy and Matt set out for a four-day hike in the desert, carrying all their supplies. Matt noticed that Randy was lugging a heavy car door and asked him why. Randy replied: "So that when I get hot I can roll down the window."

Salesperson: "Try this new bandage. You can swim, water-ski, snorkel or scuba dive with it on!"
Injured customer: "That's great! I couldn't do any of those things before I hurt myself!"

Sherlock Holmes and his trusty associate, Watson, were on a camping trip. They had gone to bed and were lying there looking up at the sky. Holmes said, "Watson, look up and tell me what you see."

"Well, I see thousands of stars," he replied.

"And what does that tell you?" asked Holmes.

"I guess it means we're going to have another nice day tomorrow. What does it mean to you?"

"To me, it means that someone has stolen our tent."

The groundskeeper at a park heard a commotion in the lake. He saw a man thrashing around in the water and said to him, "Hey, don't you know there's no swimming allowed here?"

"I'm drowning!" screamed the man, trying to keep his head above water.

"Oh well, I guess that's allowed," said the groundskeeper.

Why couldn't the geek type on her computer?
She lost her keys.

Words to the wise: Cut the pizza in four pieces if you're not hungry enough to eat six.

Words to the wise: If you know you are going to take the wrong train, leave early.

Words to the wise: You have to be very careful if you don't know where you're going because you might not get there.

Why did the twit drink a big glass of water before dinner?
He wanted to whet his appetite.

Why did the twit smell the toonie?
He wanted to know how many scents were in it.

Why did the twit move to P.E.I.?
Because it's easy to spell.

Why do twits take so long to drive to Florida?
Because whenever they see a sign that says "clean washrooms," they do.

SHE'S SUCH A TWIT ...

She put lipstick on her forehead because she wanted to make up her mind.

She asked me what *yield* means. I said, "Slow down," and she said, "w-h-a-t d-o-e-s *y-i-e-1 -d* m-e-a-n."

She stopped at a Stop sign and waited for it to say Go.

When she took me to the airport and read the sign "Airport left," she turned around and went back home.

She thought a quarterback was a refund.

She took a straw to the Grey Cup.

She went to the drive-in to see "Closed for the Season."

She went to the Gap to fill her teeth.

When she heard that 75 percent of all crimes occur around the home, she said she was moving.

HE'S SUCH A TWIT ...

When the computer said, "Press any key to continue," he started looking for the "Any" key.

He sat in a treehouse because he wanted to be a branch manager.

He got locked out of a convertible car with the top down.

He spent 20 minutes looking at an orange juice container because it said "concentrate."

He kept a ruler by his pillow to see how long he slept.

He told me to meet him at the corner of "Walk" and "Don't Walk."

He thought a lawsuit was something you wore to court.

He thought *Corner Gas* was a place where people farted a lot.

ACTUAL QUESTIONS ASKED BY TOURISTS TO CANADA:

Will I be able to see polar bears in the street?

I want to walk from Vancouver to Toronto—can I follow the railway tracks?

Which direction is north in Canada?

I have never seen it warm on TV. How do the plants grow?

What do you do with the snow when it melts?

Do you celebrate Christmas the same time as Americans do?

PRANK SQUAD

PLASTIC VOMIT: Buy some fake plastic vomit and put it in the sink. When this stuff is wet, it looks amazingly real. Expect lots of screaming.

HEAD SOAKER: Tell someone that you can pin a glass of water to the wall. Naturally, your victim will not believe you, so you'll set out to prove it. You will need a glass (a real glass, not a paper cup) of water and a straight pin. Hold the glass up and start pinning it up—then drop the pin. Ask your victim very nicely to please pick up the pin for you. When he or she bends over to get the pin, pour the water on his or her head.

TRICKY
ONES!

If Wayne Gretzky went to Winnipeg wearing a white winter coat, and his wife went to the West Edmonton Mall, how many *w*'s are there in all?
None. There are no w's in all.

A cowboy went to a motel on Friday, stayed for two days and left on Friday. How was that possible?
His horse was named Friday.

Bet someone that they can't fit more than one piece of candy into an empty bag. You'll win the bet, because once there's a candy inside, the bag is no longer empty.

A man had worked at a factory for 25 years. Every night when he left, he would push a wheelbarrow full of straw to the guard at the gate. The guard checked the wheelbarrow, found nothing and allowed the man to leave.

On the day of his retirement, the man came to the guard, but this time with no wheelbarrow. The guard finally spoke up. "Henry," he said, "you've been coming through this gate every afternoon for 25 years with a wheelbarrow. I know you've been stealing something. Can you finally tell me what it is? It's been driving me crazy."

Henry smiled and told the guard, "Okay, I'll tell you. Wheelbarrows."

Fill three glasses with water.
Line them up in a row with
three empty glasses. Then
ask a friend to change the
arrangement of the glasses
so that no empty one is next
to a full one, and no full glass
is next to an empty one. Your
friend is allowed to move only
one glass.

Here's how it's done: You
simply pour the water out of
the second glass and into the
fifth one.

How many doughnuts can you eat on an empty stomach?

One—because after you eat it, your stomach's no longer empty.

If a man is born in Nova Scotia, grows up in Manitoba and dies in Alberta, what is he?
Dead.

A plane crashes on the New Brunswick–Maine border. Where are the survivors buried?
Nowhere. The survivors are still alive.

Is it ever correct to say "I is"?
Yes. "I is the ninth letter of the alphabet."

Make a bet with someone that they won't be able to give you a wrong answer. You'll be asking five questions. The first question can be something easy—for example, "What's your name?" The second question can be something such as, "Are you my brother?" The next questions can also be easy ones; for example, "Do you have brown eyes?" and, "How old are you?"

Before you ask the last question, say, "That's four questions I've asked so far, correct?" Chances are they'll answer "yes"—which means you win the bet.

Tell someone that you can write with your nose. They'll say it can't be done—until you take a pen and write the following three words on a piece of paper: "With my nose."

Try this everyday play on words. Say your brother asks you to make him a peanut butter sandwich. What do you say? Pretend you're a genie who has the power to transform!

Your brother: "Could you make me a peanut butter sandwich?"

You: "Abracadabra! You're a peanut butter sandwich."

The same gag works for other types of sandwiches, chocolate cakes and cups of tea. This joke is good for a few laughs, but don't do it too often or someone might start playing tricks on you!

Ed: "Do you have holes in your underwear?"
Ted: "Of course not."
Ed: "Then how do you get your feet through?"

A man is locked in a room with no way to get out. In the room are a piano, a saw, a table and a baseball bat. How could he get out?

He could take a key from the piano and unlock the door.

He could take the bat and get three strikes. Then he'd be out.

He could take the saw and cut the table in two. Then, by putting the two halves together, he would have a "hole," and he could get out.

What do you have in December that you don't have in any other month?
The letter d.

What gets wetter and wetter the more it dries?
A towel.

What goes from Z to A?
A zebra.

There was a man who was born on the fifth day of the fifth month of 1955, whose lucky number was five. On his birthday he went to the racetrack and was astounded to see that in the fifth race (scheduled for five o'clock) a horse called Pentagram was running, with odds of 55 to 1. Rushing off to the bank, the man was astonished to find he had $5,555.55 in his bank account. He withdrew the whole amount, dashed back to the races and bet all of it on Pentagram to win.

Pentagram, obviously, came in fifth.

TRY THESE ON A FRIEND:

You: "What's it called when the appendix is removed?"
Friend: "An appendectomy."
You: "What's it called when the tonsils are removed?"
Friend: "A tonsillectomy."
You: "And what's it called when a growth from the head is removed?"
Friend: "I don't know."
You: "A haircut!"

You: "What's one and one?"
Friend: "Two."
You: "What's four minus two?"
Friend: "Two?"
You: "What's Shania's last name?"
Friend: "Twain."
You: "Now say it all together."
Friend: "Two, two, Twain."

You: "Have a nice twip."

What's the capital of Alberta?
A.

Why do magicians do so well in school?
They're good at trick questions.

PRANK SQUAD

FAKE BUGS: Buy them at a joke store—
they come in handy for various occa-
sions. You can freeze them in ice
cubes, and then add the cubes to
your guests' favourite drinks.

BIG-SISTER GAG: Work your big sister into a lather! Tell her that one
of her friends called (for this to
work, be specific—use the real name
of someone your sibling is close to)
and said one of the coolest kids at
school is having a party tonight,
but you can't remember all the
details. Then run and hide for the
rest of the day.

PET PEEVES

Billy: "This morning I woke up and felt the dog licking my face."
Millie: "What's wrong with that?"
Billy: "We don't have a dog."

What do you get when you cross Lassie with a rose?
A collie flower.

Mrs. Gumbo was backing out of her driveway when she heard a thump. She stopped the car and rushed out to see what had happened. At the end of the driveway was a small dog lying on its side. It was dead. Mrs. Gumbo felt awful. She knew it was her neighbour's dog. So she climbed the stairs of her neighbour's house and knocked on the door. A tall man answered. "I'm so sorry," Mrs. Gumbo said. "I was backing out of my driveway when I heard a thump. I got out to see what had happened. Your dog was lying dead at the end of the driveway. I feel terrible about it. I *insist* on replacing her."

The tall man paused and then said, "Well, I guess you can bring me my slippers and newspaper tomorrow morning."

**Boy: "What happened to the guy who stole your dog?"
Girl: "He was charged with petty theft."**

Jenny: "Did you know I'm the teacher's pet?"
Penny: "Why? Can't she afford a dog?"

Kate: "My dog has no nose."
Allie: "How does he smell?"
Kate: "Terrible."

Paul: "You play Scrabble with your dog? He must be really smart."
Jim: "Not really. I usually win."

Michael: "I lost my dog."
Karen: "Why don't you put a notice in the newspaper?"
Michael: "He can't read."

Steve: "My pet kangaroo can't wait till it's 2012."
Don: "Why's that?"
Steve: "It's a leap year."

One day a man walked into a bird shop carrying a beak. "I'm looking for a bird to match this beak," he said.

"No problem," said the store owner. "I've got one that'll fit the bill."

Pat: "I just bought a parrot for $500."
Matt: "Does it talk?"
Pat: "Yeah."
Matt: "So what does it say?"
Pat: "'You paid too much. You paid too much.'"

Lisa decided to call her dog Stripe. Her friend Will looked at her like she was crazy. "Why did you call your dog Stripe?" asked Will. "He's a Dalmatian with black spots."

"Well, my other pet is named Spot," explained Lisa.

"You never told me you had another Dalmatian," said Will.

"I don't. My other pet is a zebra."

Three boys watched a fire truck roar down the street with a beautiful Dalmatian riding on top of it. The first boy said, "They use him to pull children to safety."

"You're wrong," said the second boy. "He helps keep people away from the fire."

"Both of you are wrong," said the third. "They use him to find the fire hydrant."

What did the 500-kilogram canary say as he walked down the street?
"Here, kitty, kitty, kitty."

Two mothers were comparing stories about their children. The first one complained that her son never wanted to get out of bed in the morning. The second told her, "I don't have that problem. When it's time for my son to get up, I just throw the cat in his bed."

"How does that help?" asked the first mom.

"He sleeps with the dog."

Mike got a parrot for his birthday. The parrot had a bad attitude and an even worse vocabulary. Every other word was rude. Mike tried to change the bird's manners, but nothing worked.

One day, Mike felt so desperate that he put the parrot in the freezer. At first the bird squawked, then suddenly everything was quiet. Mike was frightened that he might have hurt the bird and quickly opened the freezer door. The parrot calmly stepped out onto his arm and said, "I'm sorry if I have offended you, and I ask for your forgiveness. I will behave better." Mike was amazed at the great change in the bird and was about to ask what had caused it when the parrot continued: "May I ask what the chicken did?"

A dad goes into a pet store and asks if he can return the puppy he got for his son. The owner replies, "I'm sorry, sir, but we've already sold your son to someone else."

A man bought his wife a talking bird for her birthday. It spoke seven languages and cost him a month's pay. "Well," he asked her when he got home, "did you get the bird I sent you?"

"Yes," answered his wife. "I already have it in the oven."

"What! That bird could speak seven languages!" said the man, upset.

"Then why didn't it say anything?"

What did the cat get on the test?

A purrfect score.

What do you call a cat who can bowl?
An alley cat.

What do you call a small cat that makes up songs?
An itty bitty ditty kitty.

What do you call an over-weight cat?
A flabby tabby.

What do you get when you cross a cat with a ball of wool?
Mittens.

What do you have to be careful of when it rains cats and dogs?
That you don't step in a poodle.

What dog loves to have its fur washed?
A shampoodle.

What's better than a talking dog?
A spelling bee.

Where can you leave your dog while you shop?
In the barking lot.

Why did the cat family move next door to the mouse family?
So they could have the neighbours for dinner.

Why did the Doberman marry the Golden Retriever?
He found her very fetching.

Why was the cat so small?
Because it drank only condensed milk.

Why wouldn't the canary pay for his date's dinner?
He was too cheap.

Why wouldn't the pet store take back the chimp?
They didn't offer a monkey-back guarantee.

A woman goes into a pet store one day. "I'm really lonely," she says to the clerk. "I need a pet to keep me company."

"Well," replies the clerk, "how about this nice parrot? He'll talk to you."

"Hey, that's great," says the woman. She buys the parrot and takes him home. The next day the woman comes back to the pet store.

"You know, that parrot isn't talking to me yet," she says.

"Hmm, let's see," says the clerk. "I know! Buy this little ladder for his cage. He'll climb the ladder, and then he'll talk." So off she goes with the newly purchased ladder. The next day she comes back again.

"Hey, that parrot still hasn't said a word," she says to the clerk.

He thinks a minute. "How about this little mirror?" he says. "Hang it at the top of the ladder. The parrot will climb the ladder, look in the mirror, and then he'll talk to you."

The next day the same woman comes back to the pet shop, and she is very distressed.

"What's wrong?" asks the clerk.

"My parrot . . . well, he died," she answers quietly.

"Oh my gosh! I'm so sorry for your loss!" exclaims the clerk. "But I have to ask you, did the parrot ever say anything to you?"

"Oh, yes, he said one thing, right before he died," she replies. "He said, 'Doesn't that store sell any food?'"

PRANK SQUAD

COLD-WATER TORTURE: Pour cold water over the top of the shower curtain rod onto someone using the shower. Run away fast.

PHONE FUN: Try these greetings the next time you answer the phone:

"[Your name]'s Pizza! I'm the guy if you want pie!"

"Pet's Vets! There's no business like monkey business!"

"Hello, Disco Cat, the place for glitter and litter!"

"Wine Cellar! We love to complain!"

(In a whisper) "Institute for Overly Sensitive Eardrums."

LIMERICKS
AND TONGUE
TWISTERS

There was an old man with a beard
Who said, "This is just as I feared.
A gull and a wren,
Two owls and a hen
Are building a nest in my beard."

There was a young lady from Leeds
Who swallowed a package of seeds.
Within half an hour
Her nose was a flower.
And her head a bundle of weeds.

There once was a man from Peru
Who dreamed he was eating his shoe.
He woke up one night
In a terrible fright,
And found it was perfectly true.

There was a young lady named Wright.
Whose speed was much faster than
   light.
She set out one day
In a relative way
And returned on the previous night.

A tutor who tooted the flute
Tutored two tooters to toot.
Said the two to the tutor,
"Is it easier to toot or
To tutor two tooters to toot?"

A lady from old Montreal
Wore a newspaper dress to a ball.
The dress caught fire
And burned her entire
Front page, sports section and all.

There once was a man from Quebec
Who wrapped both his legs round
    his neck.
But then he forgot
How to untie the knot,
And now he is just such a wreck.

There was a young man from the Soo
Who found a large mouse in his stew.
Said the waiter, "Don't shout
And wave it about,
Or the rest will be wanting one too."

There was a young lady named Rose
Who had a large wart on her nose
When she had it removed,
Her appearance improved
But her glasses slipped down to
    her toes.

An elderly man named Keith
Misplaced his set of false teeth.
They were left on a chair,
He forgot they were there,
And sat down and was bitten beneath.

WE DARE YOU TO TRY SAYING EACH TONGUE TWISTER THREE TIMES FAST:

Can canned clams can clams?

Feeble felines fear fur.

Six sharp smart sharks.

She freed six sick sheep.

Fat frogs flying fast.

Selfish shellfish.

TRY SAYING THESE JUST ONCE:

The fifth fink sinks faster than the first four finks think.

Such a silly tongue twister mustn't be mumbled.

Which witch watched which witch's watch walk?

Sneaking in my creaky squeaky reeking sneakers.

Bee stings sting severely when it's sunburned skin that's stung.

Kent sent Trent the rent to rent
Trent's tent.

Sally saw Shelley singing swinging
summer swimming songs.

The ocean sure soaked Sherman.

PRANK SQUAD

CEREAL SNEAKERS: Leave dry cereal in the toes of your friend's shoes—add some crunch to someone's step!

PIZZA PARLOUR TORMENT:
1. Ask for the crust on top this time.
2. Ask if you get to keep the pizza box when you're done. When they say yes, act very relieved.
3. Pretend you know the person on the phone. Say something like, "Hey, your voice sounds familiar . . . I think we went to poop camp together about five years ago!"
4. Make the first topping you order pepperoni. Just before you hang up, say, "Remember—no pepperoni, please!"

SHAGGY-DOG
STORIES
AND OTHER
GROANERS

Shaggy-dog jokes are those overly long and annoying stories that make you groan because they're full of meaningless details and absurd characters. In fact, most of the story has little relation to the punchline. A good storyteller, though, can have people in stitches because the ending is often so stupid and unexpected. Shaggy-dog jokes get their name from an old, long and pointless joke about a shaggy dog. Today, however, the stories can be about anything, as long as they are ridiculous and lengthy and told in a misleading way.

A girl was walking in the dark one night when she heard a *bump bump* behind her. She started moving faster, but the *bump bump* continued. When she turned around, she was startled to see a giant coffin bouncing in her direction. She ran all the way home, through the front gate and up the steps to her door where, after struggling with her keys, she finally managed to get inside and lock the door behind her. But just as she got inside, the coffin came crashing in and chased her up the staircase! She locked herself in the washroom, but the coffin smashed through the door. Determined to survive, she grabbed a bottle of cough syrup in the medicine cabinet. Desperate, she threw it at the coffin.

And the coffin stopped.

A business was looking for office help. The owner put a sign in the window that read, "Help wanted. Must be good with a computer and must be bilingual." A little later, a dog trotted up to the window and went inside. The manager looked surprised and said, "I can't hire you. The sign says you must be good with a computer."

The dog went to the computer and typed out a perfect letter. The manager was stunned but then told the dog, "I realize that you are a very capable dog. However, I *still* can't give you the job. The sign also says that you must speak two languages."

The dog looked calmly at the manager and said, "Meow."

A camel, a giraffe and a pig all went to an audition at a comedy club. The camel went on first. He did an impersonation of a llama and told 10 jokes. The judges all laughed. Then the giraffe came out. First the giraffe cleared her throat. Then she did a headstand and told a few tall tales. The judges found her funny too. Then the pig stood at the microphone. He told a really, really, really long story about a circus dog. The joke was so long that it took the pig two hours to tell it. The judges were so upset that they threw the pig out of the club.

Why didn't the judges like the pig?

The pig was a real boar.

A frog went to a bank to apply for a loan. Patty Stack, the woman in charge of loans, asked if he had anything to leave for collateral. "Don't worry," she said. "When you pay back the loan, we'll return it to you." He showed her a small porcelain statue and said, "This is what I have. It is a family heirloom, and it's very special to me."

She took it to the bank manager and said, "There's a frog out there who wants a loan, and this is what he gave me as proof that we can trust him, but I don't know what it is. Should I give him the money?"

The bank manager said, "Why, that's a knick-knack, Patty Stack. Give that frog a loan."

A genius was working on a new invention. It was such a great machine that it could perform a variety of tasks at once. It could water a garden, pour milk, sew buttons on a coat, scrub dishes, squirt ketchup, walk the dog, solve math problems, play hockey, fold laundry, make hot-fudge sundaes, clean the cat's litter box and answer the phone. The genius had all the parts laid out in front of her but needed something to put the machine together. So she sent her dumb assistant to the store to buy some glue. The store had almost everything: toothpaste, breaded halibut, licorice, but no glue. The assistant wasn't upset. She bought the breaded halibut.

How come?

It doesn't take a genius to know fish sticks.

Once upon a time, in a magical land, there lived a snake named Nate. In this land, close to Nate's house, there was a great road, and next to this road was an ancient lever. According to myth, if the lever was pushed, it would trigger the end of the world. One day, Nate was slithering down the road. When he reached the lever, he began to cross the road. At the same moment, a truck came zooming around the corner, and the driver found himself in a dilemma: either hit the snake and run him over, or swerve, hit the lever and end the world. Needless to say, the driver ran Nate over and drove away. What's the moral of this story? *Better Nate than lever.*

One September, some grade three children came into their classroom to discover the new teacher was a stallion. He was a big stallion, but he had a high-pitched, little voice, and the class thought this was hilarious. They laughed every time he opened his mouth, and he spent the whole day yelling and screaming for order. Finally the stallion lost his voice, and the next day he brought a pony into the class to help him out. The pony was small, but he had a voice like a foghorn, and he bellowed, "YOU KIDS PAY ATTENTION OR ELSE!"

The kids quieted down and paid attention, which only goes to show: To get things done you have to shout until you get a little hoarse.

The TV game show was close. One contestant was just 200 points behind the leader, and the host was about to ask him the final question, worth 500 points.

"To win," the host said, "name two of Santa's reindeer."

The contestant smiled because it was such an easy question. "Rudolph!" he said confidently. "And Olive!"

The confused host said, "We'll accept Rudolph, but could you please explain Olive?"

The man looked impatiently at the host and said, "You know: 'Olive, the other reindeer, used to laugh and call him names . . . '"

There was once a young prince in a far-away land who was very much loved by his parents. The king and queen would take him to the circus and feed him all the cakes and pies he wanted. When the prince got a little older, however, he started to rebel. He hung around with the wrong subjects and strayed far from the castle on his own. One day in the forest, he was ambushed by an evil warlock who changed him into a fool. The courtiers made fun of him, and his parents sent him into exile. What's the moral of the story?

Heir today, goon tomorrow.

Upon assuming power, a tribal chief who had a soft spot for animals forbade the killing of any creature. Before long, however, the number of lions and cheetahs was getting out of hand. There were so many of them that they did not have enough to eat and began feeding on humans. The people were terrified and asked their leader to reverse his order, but he refused. The people decided they had no choice but to overthrow the chief.

It was the first time in history that a reign was called on account of game.

A man was driving down a lonely country road when it began to snow heavily. The car's windows fogged up, and the wiper blades, which were badly worn, soon fell apart. The man couldn't see the road anymore, so he stopped the car. Then he got out and started to turn over some large rocks by the side of the road. Finally, he found two frozen snakes. He straightened them out and stuck them flat onto his blades, and they worked just fine.

Haven't you ever heard of wind-chilled vipers?

A frog meets a fairy.

"For 40 bucks," the fairy says, "I can turn you into a prince."

So the frog gives the fairy 50 dollars.

The fairy changes the frog into a handsome prince. The former frog is overjoyed.

"It'll be easier to get a date for the ball," he thinks.

The prince asks the fairy for the remaining 10 dollars so he can rent a limo to get to the ball. The fairy gives him the money and then the prince shrinks in his boots, turns green and is once again a frog. Shocked, the frog stares at the fairy. "What happened?" he croaks.

"Well," she replies, "you gave me 50 bucks and then asked for your change back."

A man heard his friend was in the hospital but didn't know what had happened to him, or even which room to visit. So he went to the hospital and politely waited at the desk. When the nurse behind the desk looked up, the man gave his friend's name and asked for the room number. "Room 105, 106, 107 and 108," the nurse replied and went back to her paperwork.

"I don't understand," the man stammered. "Which one is it?"

"All of them," the nurse said. "He got run over by a steamroller."

A man is sitting at home when the doorbell rings. He answers the door to find a six-foot-tall cockroach standing there. The cockroach punches him and runs off. The next evening, the man is at home again when the doorbell rings. He answers, and the same cockroach is outside. This time, it kicks and karate-chops him before running away. The injured man crawls to the phone and calls an ambulance. He is rushed to the hospital and treated, and a doctor asks him what happened. The man explains the attacks by the six-foot-tall cockroach. The doctor thinks for a moment and says, "Yes, I hear there's a nasty bug going around."

A man who had been working for the circus for many years as Mr. Tiny, the shortest man alive, agreed to meet with a local newspaper reporter one Sunday to be interviewed. The reporter arrived on time but was surprised to be greeted by a man who towered over him. The reporter thought he must be in the wrong place and asked for Mr. Tiny.

"That's me," said the man.

"But you're supposed to be short!" said the reporter.

Mr. Tiny said, "I told you—this is my day off."

A woman walked into a bar with a monster on a leash.

"Sorry," said the bartender, "but that creature looks dangerous. You'll have to tie it up outside."

The woman took the monster outside, then came back and ordered a drink. She was just finishing it when a man came into the bar and said, "Whose monster is that outside?"

"Mine," said the woman proudly.

"Well, I'm sorry," the man said, "but my dog just killed your monster."

"Killed him! What kind of dog do you have?"

"A Yorkie," said the man.

"But how could a Yorkie kill my great big monster?"

"She got stuck in his throat and choked him!"

An elephant was drinking out of a river one day when he spotted a turtle asleep on a log. He marched over and kicked it clear across the river. "What did you do that for?" asked a giraffe that happened to be passing by.

"Because I recognized it as the same turtle that took a nip out of my trunk 53 years ago."

"Wow, what a memory!" exclaimed the giraffe.

"Yes," said the elephant. "It's a case of turtle recall."

A man sitting in a movie theatre notices that there is a bear sitting next to him. Eventually he turns to the bear and says, "Aren't you a bear?"

The bear nods, so the man says, "So what are you doing at the movies?"

The bear says, "Well, I liked the book."

Mary Poppins moved to California and starts a business telling people's fortunes. But she doesn't read palms or tea leaves, she smells a person's breath. The sign outside reads: "Super California Mystic, Expert Halitosis."

Two little skunks, one named In and one named Out, wanted to go outside and play. Their parents told them they could, but an hour later, only Out came back.

"Hasn't In come in?" asked Father Skunk.

"Out went out with In but only Out came back in," said Mother Skunk.

"Well, Out," said Father, "you better go out and find In and bring her in."

So Out did. And only a few moments later, he returned with his wayward sister.

"Ah, good," said Mother Skunk, pleased. "How did you find her?"

Out smiled. "Instinct," he said.

Man to stranger on street: "Excuse me, sir, you have a sausage in your ear."

Stranger: "Sorry?"

Man: "I said you have a sausage in your ear."

Stranger: "Can you say that again?"

Man (shouting): "You have a sausage in your ear."

Stranger (shaking his head): "Sorry, I can't hear you. I have a sausage in my ear."

PRANK SQUAD

STUCK ON CASH:
Beginner version: Use superglue to attach a quarter to the sidewalk at a place where it's safe to stop. Watch people try to pick it up.

Advanced version: Attach a five-dollar bill to a long piece of fishing line. Pull it along the sidewalk and watch people try to grab it. If someone comes close, jerk the fishing line and pull it out of his or her reach while you hide.

ELEVATOR FREAK-OUT: Stand silently in a corner, facing the wall. There is scientific proof that if you do this long enough, the other passengers will all turn and face the wall too.

A GRAB BAG
OF RIDDLES

A monkey, a bear, a cockatoo, a gerbil and a rhinoceros all stood under the same umbrella. Who got wet?
Nobody. It wasn't raining.

At what time did Dracula go to the dentist?
Tooth hurty.

Can you telephone from an airplane?
Yes—the telephone is the one with the dial tone.

How did the giant's wife know that Jack was coming?

She could hear Jack and the beans talk.

What do you carve on a robot's tombstone?
Rust in peace.

Where did the snowman take his snow-wife to dance?
A snowball.

What costs a dollar and goes to the moon?
A loonie module.

Why are perfume salespeople so smart? They have good scents.

Do old history teachers ever marry?
No, they just get dated.

Does a roller coaster like its work?
It has its ups and downs.

How come aliens don't drown in hot chocolate? They sit on the Mars-mallows.

How does a bee get to school?
It takes the buzz.

How is a basketball player like a baby?
They both dribble.

How many successful jumps do you need to make before graduating from parachute school?
All of them.

How much fun can you have doing arithmetic?
Sum fun.

What day does a fish hate the most?
Fryday.

What did Isaac Newton say when that apple fell on his head?
Ouch!

What did the astronaut think of the takeoff?
She thought it was a blast.

What did the paint give the wall on their first anniversary?
A new coat.

What did the termite do when she couldn't carry the twig on her own? She hired an assist-ant.

What do 18-wheelers say on Halloween?
Truck or treat.

How can you get four suits for a toonie?
Buy a deck of cards.

What do angels say when they answer the telephone?
"Halo!"

What do cats call mice?
Delicious.

What do cats drink on hot summer afternoons?
Miced tea.

How did the computers buy a new car?
They all chipped in.

What's a dancer's favourite province?
The Bossa Nova Scotia.

What's a musician's favourite province?
Manituba.

Where does low-fat milk come from?
Skinny cows.

What do diplomats say on Halloween?
Trick or treaty.

What do farmers plant in their sofas?
Couch potatoes.

What do math teachers eat?
Square meals.

What do mermaids have on toast?
Mermalade.

What do pirates eat for dinner?
Fish and ships.

What do sharks eat at barbecues?
Clamburgers.

What do squirrels say on Halloween?
Trick or tree.

What do Tarzan and Jane sing at Christmastime?
"Jungle Bells."

What do you say if an abominable snowman is about to chomp your head off?
"Chill, dude."

What do you say to an angry monster?
"Hey, no need to bite my head off!"

What does a computer programmer eat for lunch?
An Apple.

What does a reptile wear on its feet?
Snakers.

What does a viper do after it sneezes?
It vipes its nose.

What does an astronaut use to dust those hard-to-reach black holes?
A vacuum cleaner.

What does Tim Hortons give to new employees?
A list of do's and dough-not's.

What goes zzub, zzub, zzub?
A bee flying backward.

What happened to the guy who couldn't keep up on the payments to his exorcist?
He was re-possessed.

What happened to the house built of cymbals?
The whole thing came crashing down.

What happened when the dry cleaner was mugged?
He pressed charges.

What happens to astronauts who misbehave?
They're grounded.

What is a pop machine's favourite dance?
The can-can.

What is a shark's favourite game?
Swallow the leader.

What is the heaviest kind of soup?
Wonton soup.

What is the largest ant on Earth?
An elephant.

What kind of bow is impossible to tie?
A rainbow.

What kind of fish goes with peanut butter?
Jelly fish.

What kind of lizard loves to tell jokes?
A silly-mander.

What kind of trains do ballerinas take?
Tutu trains.

What kind of TV do you find in a haunted house? A big-scream TV.

What kind of waves are impossible to swim in?
Microwaves.

What made the newspaper blush?
It saw the comic strip.

What nail does a carpenter hate to hit?
Her thumbnail.

What part of the keyboard do astronauts like best?
The space bar.

What's a cat's favourite colour?
Purrrple.

What's fast, furry and goes "foow, foow"?
A dog chasing a car that's in reverse.

What's in the middle of a jellyfish?
A jellybutton.

What's it called when you stop the car and make your annoying brother get out?
A pest stop.

What's the magic word for getting rid of scabs?
Scabracadabra!
Does it work?
Scabsolutely.

What's the world's second-oldest rock group? The Rolling Flintstones.

When is a tire a bad singer?
When it's flat.

When is fishing not a good way to relax?
When you're the worm.

When should you bring your father to class?
When you have a pop quiz.

Where do fish go on vacation?
To Finland.

Where do spies go shopping?
At a snooper market.

Where do you find France?
On a map.

Who is the best-paid employee at Microsoft?
The Windows washer.

Who was the worst-tempered composer ever?
Ludwig van Beastoven.

Why are riddles like pencils?
They're no good unless they have a point.

Why aren't babies allowed to take tests?
Because they all have crib sheets.

Why can't you sleep during band practice?
Because it's too noisy.

Why couldn't the tire quit its job?
It was flat broke.

Why did all the bees in the hive start throwing up?
There was a bug going around.

Why did the fish stop smoking cigarettes?
It didn't want to get hooked.

Why did the praying mantis go to the film?
It heard it was a feeler-good movie.

Why do birds fly south in the winter?
It beats waiting for a ride.

Why do blue cheeses look alike?

They're all cut from the same mould.

Why do ghosts make great cheerleaders?
They have lots of spirit.

Why do nuns like Swiss cheese the best?
Because it's holey.

Why do refrigerators hum?
Because they don't know the words.

Why do spiders do so well in computer class?
They love the Web.

Why does the toast like the knife?
Because the knife butters him up.

Why doesn't a python use silverware?
Because it has a forked tongue.

Why don't computers eat anything?
They don't like what's on their menus.

Why is football so popular on Venus? Because all the houses have Astroturf on their front lawns.

Why is Homer Simpson bad at singing scales?
He always gets stuck at "Doh!"

Why is it good to tell ghost stories in hot weather?
Because they are so chilling.

Why is it so hard to fool a snake?
Because you can't pull its leg.

Why is monastery food so greasy?
It's all cooked by friars.

Why shouldn't you hang a funny picture on your wall?
The plaster might crack up.

Why shouldn't you take your computer into rush-hour traffic?
Because it might crash.

Why was Cinderella thrown off the baseball team?
She kept running away from the ball.

Why was everyone worried about the small bucket?
It was a little pail.

Why was the couch afraid of the chair?
The chair was armed.

Why was the dresser embarrassed?
Its drawers fell down.

Why was the firefighter lovesick?
She couldn't get over an old flame.

Why was the math book sad?
It had too many problems.

Why was the nail so unhappy?
The carpenter kept hitting it on the head.

Why was the pantry so good at telling the future?
It knew what was in store.

Why was the saucepan always getting in trouble?
It was too hot to handle.

Why was the space-craft reading the horoscopes?
It was a Gemini.

Why wouldn't the girl mouse move in with the boy mouse?
Because his house was such a hole in the wall.

What has a broom and flies?
A jam-covered janitor.

How do baby birds know how to fly?
They just wing it.

How do you keep a fool busy all day?
Put him in a round room and tell him to sit in the corner.

During which school period do cars get put together?
Assembly.

How did the computer feel after its memory had been upgraded?
Chipper.

How did the scientist invent bug spray?
She started from scratch.

If an athlete gets athlete's foot, what does a lifeguard get?
Undertoe.

If athletes get athlete's foot, what do astronauts get?
Missile-toe.

What accidents happen every 24 hours?
Day breaks and night falls.

What climbs trees without a sound and has feet that always touch the ground?
A vine.

What did Dorothy do when her dog got stuck?
She called a Toto truck.

Why couldn't the Tin Man join in the card game?
They were playing Hearts.

What do they serve at the cyber café?
Silicon chips with dip.

What do you put in a barrel to make it lighter?
A hole.

What do you throw out when you need it and take in when you don't need it?
An anchor.

What driver doesn't need a licence?
A screwdriver.

What makes Jackie Chan sick every winter?
Kung flu.

What has a head and a tail but no body?
A coin.

What has teeth but doesn't bite? A comb.

What is the largest building in Transylvania?
The Vampire State Building.

What kind of music do long-distance truckers listen to?
Cross-country music.

What kind of music do they play at Stonehenge?
Hard rock.

What kind of music do they play at a playground?
Swing.

What kind of music do they play at a soft-drink factory?
Pop.

What kind of music do they play at a construction site?
Heavy metal.

What kind of school does Sherlock Holmes attend?
Elementary, my dear Watson.

What stands in New York, holds a torch and sneezes a lot? The Ah-Choo of Liberty.

What's in the middle of Ontario?
The letter a.

When is a tuba good for your teeth?
When it's a tuba toothpaste.

Where did the Arabian knights live? In sand castles.

Where do lettuces practise law?
At the salad bar.

Where is the ocean deepest?
At the bottom.

Which movie director always forgets to wear sunblock?
Steven Peelberg.

Why are cowboys bad at math?
They're always rounding things up.

Why are lost things always in the last place you look?
Because when you find them, you stop looking.

Why are the Knights of the Round Table so cheap?
They're always cutting corners.

Why couldn't Noah catch many fish while he was on the Ark?
Because he only had two worms.

Why was the computer geek disappointed by the zoo?
He couldn't find any RAM.

Why was the computer so tired when it got home from the office?
Because it had a hard drive.

Why was the library so tall?
Because it had so many storeys!

What's the definition of ignorance?
I don't know.

Why didn't the salad joke make it into this book?
It got tossed.